The View from a Distant Star

The View from a Distant Star

Man's Future in the Universe

by HARLOW SHAPLEY

Basic Books, Inc.
Publishers
NEW YORK | LONDON

Second Printing

© 1963 by Basic Books, Inc., Publishers

Library of Congress Catalog Card Number 63–18673

Manufactured in the United States of America

Designed by Sophie Adler

Preface

Mankind is made of star stuff, ruled by universal laws. The thread of cosmic evolution runs through his history, as through all phases of the universe—the microcosmos of atomic structures, molecular forms, and microscopic organisms, and the macrocosmos of higher organisms, of planets, stars, and galaxies. Evolution is still proceeding in galaxies and man—to what end, we can only vaguely surmise.

Is man here to stay? Can he survive the rigors of his harsh environment? He has himself made it harsh by adding to the natural hazards greater ones of his own making. Population pressures and the fruits of his science and technology now threaten his future. His lifetime on our small planet will depend on how well he understands the requirements for survival and how willing he is to struggle for the peaceful creation of a viable world society.

This volume considers our species in the vast frame of the universe at large. The opening chapters describe mankind's place in space, time, and evolution, and in relation to other life on this and other planets. We go on to explore man's problems of co-existence—cosmic and terrestrial. We dwell

v

a bit on the exciting capacities and education of the human mind, not overlooking its diverting foibles, such as astrology, saucer flying, water dowsing, and other Dark Arts. Finally, in the concluding chapters we picture a Psychozoic Kingdom offering rich goals for evolving man.

Many of the chapters are based on lectures and on articles that I have written in recent years, all of them now reworked and, where necessary, brought up to date. For example, the chapter called "The Human Response to an Expanding Universe" is developed from an essay originally published in the *Hibbert Journal* in 1959; "One World of Stars" is based on my presidential address at the centennial meeting of the American Association for the Advancement of Science; the chapter "A Design for Fighting" is based on a Phi Beta Kappa address to that Association; it was printed in the *American Scholar* and later in several magazines and anthologies and, in part, in the *Congressional Record*.

I am glad to acknowledge my debt to the many associates who have in conversations over the years unknowingly assisted in the maturing of my ideas on cosmogonic matters.

H.S.

Contents

The View from a Distant Star

1

Two Moments
of Discovery

Man's intellectual history has been marked by many moments of sudden revelation, both in science and in philosophy. Some moments stand out as turning points in his understanding of human existence and of its place in the scheme of things. All through the fields of science we recognize such moments and the consequent solving of puzzling problems. Two such occasions in my own personal experience have considerably affected my world-view. A brief report on them will serve to illustrate some methods in scientific research, and at the same time introduce this discussion of cosmographic matters.

The first revealing moment that I shall describe occurred many years ago during my studies of variable stars, star

1

clusters, and galaxies. For several years my technical assistants and I had been measuring the distances, sizes, and motions of certain globular star clusters. Using the best telescopic equipment then in existence, we had made thousands of observations. It turned out that the distances of the globular clusters were astoundingly great—greater than the supposed diameter of the whole stellar universe. Finally came the day for a critical overall examination and integration of our data, and it led to an astonishing conclusion.

Talking to myself and to the colleague who was refereeing my researches, I was explaining:

"And now, from the plot of the positions of these globular star clusters, projected on the galactic plane, you can see this peculiar asymmetry—this lop-sided distribution, which probably means. . . . Good Heavens! It means that the center of the universe may be away off in the Sagittarius direction, tens of thousands of light-years distant. Wonderful! Or is it?"

It was a shocking thought—this sudden realization that the center of our universe was not where we stood but far off in space, that our heliocentric picture of the universe must be replaced by a strange sort of eccentric universe.

Gradually a reorienting view developed: "I have put it wrong end to. I should not say or think that the center of our universe is so remote and removed from us, so remote from the proud observers. No, I should say that the trivial observer is far from the magnificent, star-filled center! He is the peripheral, the ephemeral one. He is the incidental biological by-product of water, soil, air, and sunlight. He is off in a cosmic corner, invisible from the central nucleus around which billions of stars revolve and to which we, like they, pay gravitational homage."

It was for me a new world: a world that was exhibiting a stupendous show, with most of the action elsewhere and we but confused bystanders watching the play and noting a few of the more obvious facts. This planet's mankind could no longer seriously call itself "Lords of Creation." Instead, let us dwell thoughtfully on the hundred billion stars of the Milky Way, contemplate the stellar bodies a billion times the size of our sun, consider the nebulae and the great clusters of galaxies, and remember the millions of centuries that our planet existed before man appeared and began to blink with primeval wondering about heaven's scintillating lights.

The intimations of mankind's inconsequentiality, incited that day by the plot of the globular star clusters on the galactic plane, made a strong and indelible impact. Actually we should not have needed the sidereal revelations to correct our vanity. Microcosmically, as well as macrocosmically, nature's phenomena might well inspire humility in us human observers. The microscope shows sights and incites ideas which should put us in our place. Somehow, however, the microcosmic world of electrons, cells, light quanta, and bacteria fails to awe us. We feel superior to the swift little activities in phototube or mouse.

But the large-scale handiworks of Omnipotence have always troubled our self-esteem. (I am speaking here for the more educated primates.) Years ago we Romans did not like to give up the idea that Rome was the center of the world. Later we resisted in spirit and argument the shift of the cosmic center from the earth to the sun. We had cherished that geocentric theory of the universe, and the importance it had given us. And now we liked even less the subordination of our own little solar system to a majestic center far off beyond the bright stars of Sagittarius. This shift in world concept began to shake the stuffiness out of us. It is still uncomfortable to many religionists and others. Heaven knows, we cherish our stuffiness!

Let us return to those globular star clusters and see what they told us.

Until the present century, astronomers had little means of measuring the distances of the stars in the sky with accuracy or to any great depth. The traditional method of trigonometry (using the diameter of the earth's orbit as a baseline) gave the distances of only those relatively few stars within a few hundred light-years of us. As a consequence, most astronomers did not concern themselves much with speculation about the dimensions of the universe. Their guess was that the visible stars (seen with the naked eye or telescopes) formed a system extending out perhaps a few thousand light-years, with the sun at or near the center.

Two centuries ago Immanuel Kant and Thomas Wright did recognize that the Milky Way band was composed of stars, and surmised that the blobs of light called nebulae might be more distant stellar systems, so far away that their individual stars could not be distinguished. In the nineteenth century popular writers occasionally spoke of external galaxies, with the intimation that the universe might be considerably bigger than had been supposed. But the professional astronomers, busy with difficult technical details of sidereal exploration and measurement, were content to hold to the heliocentric view of the stellar system. The nature and dimensions of the whole universe were left for speculators and philosophers to dream about.

THE CEPHEIDS

Then came a new development—a new method of measuring the distances of stars which was worked out early in this century. It was the photometric method based on the variations in brightness of the pulsating stars known as the Cepheids. I had the good fortune to take part, along with many others, in that exciting episode of discovery. We had a good time, both the protagonists and the critics, in this "sky-breaking" work.

The story of the Cepheids is long and well-known. Here I need only say that these bodies are the most important giant stars in the sky. Named for the constellation of Cepheus because they imitate the star Delta in that constellation in the way they brighten and dim in regular periods, they provide us with an invaluable measuring stick. From their period-luminosity relation we were able to deduce their absolute brightness and eventually their distances. Not only do they tell us their distances, and the distance of any group of stars that contains Cepheids, but they also give us suggestions as to the evolution of stellar bodies and the nature of the radiation from stellar surfaces. Fortunately for us, and for our knowledge of the universe, Cepheid variables show up in many star systems, as well as in the neighborhood of our solar system and in the Milky Way.

It was with the help of the Cepheids that we found the distances of the globular star clusters, the dimensions of our galaxy, and, as a small detail, our position on the outskirts of the galaxy. After two or three years of work on these stars, it became apparent that the universe was uncomfortably larger, more populous, and more inscrutable than we had supposed. Either that, or our methods and observations had trapped us in some fallacious deductions. There were indeed some fallacies and traps, chief of which was the fact, then little recognized, that there is much starlight-absorbing dust and gas between the stars, which leads astronomers to erroneous measurements of brightness and distance.

But there was no major fallacy. There was no getting around the fact that the new techniques revealed, for example, that the great star cluster in Hercules was some 30,000 light-years distant. This was a distance greater than we had known about in all the previous measurements on isolated stars. It also gave us firm evidence of a large lapse of time, for the light we were photographing was more than 30,000 years old.

Here indeed was raw material for cosmic cogitation. The light just arriving from one of the nearest of the globular clusters had been traveling through space for 300 centuries. This Herculean light had already covered four-fifths of its 180,000,000,000,000,000,000-mile journey to the earth before the first human civilizations on this planet were born; during the last one-fifth of its trip most of man's civilization have had time to grow up, decay, and vanish.

It took some years to identify the few scores of globular star clusters in the sky, to study their variable stars and thus determine their distances and positions in space, and to find that many of them were grouped rather smoothly around a point in the southern Milky Way. It then became apparent that this point was very likely the center of our galaxy, and the concept was strengthened when the astronomers Bertil Lindblad and Jan H. Oort established that the galaxy appeared to be rotating around this region.

In an early study we placed the direction of the center near the junction of the bright constellations of Scorpio,

Sagittarius, and Ophiuchus. The data were not very extensive, and it is therefore rather surprising and agreeable that the many subsequent researches, using other types of stars and clusters and other methods, have verified closely our original determination from the globular star clusters. In galactic coordinates, if you are interested, the longitude of the center is approximately 327°, latitude 0°; in equatorial coordinates it is in right ascension 17 hours 30 minutes, declination −30°.

From where we stand our Milky Way is a mess, with dense star clouds, dust clouds, and aggregations of gas all confusing the picture. Also, these various objects are in motions which are both smooth and turbulent. Further, we on the rotating earth are in motion around the sun, which is in motion with respect to the neighboring stars, which are participating with us in a long circulatory motion about the center of the galaxy. Confronted with these complicated motions, we cannot give a clear and conclusive description of the central nucleus, or a value of its distance that is correct within 5 per cent. There is an uncertainty of 10 per cent or more in the measurement of our speed around the galactic center, and similar error in our value of the duration of one revolution. For the time being we settle on a speed of some 200 miles a second (for us and the neighboring stars), and a revolution time of 200 million years. Finally, we put the total mass of our great spiral galaxy at something like 200 billion times the mass of our sun, which in turn is more than 300,000 times the mass of the earth.

All these superlatives are inserted without explanation or apology to indicate that we have, in studies of the universe, gone a long way since 1917 when we first gazed with some astonishment at the evidence that the center of our "universe"—our galaxy among the myriads of galaxies—is apparently more than 30,000 light-years from our little local abode. When someone asks me now, "What are you doing for the good of the world?", I ask, "What do you mean by 'world'?"

After extensive measuring in our own galaxy, astronomers confirmed the speculations of the eighteenth-century philosopher (Kant) and the nineteenth-century popular writers that the innumerable spiral nebulae are indeed other galaxies of stars, the overall system extending beyond the grasp of our most potent telescopes.

With the new knowledge of dimensions in our own galaxy, we quickly realized that the Metagalaxy—the galaxy of galaxies—could well be measured in units very much larger than those that suffice for the stars near enough to be seen with the naked eye. We now use as the common unit of distances in the Metagalaxy not the light-year but the mega-light-year, which is one million light-years, each light-year being 5,800,-000,000,000 miles. Or we may resort to a still larger unit—the mega-parsec, which is 3.26 mega-light-years.

After seven years of work with large instruments on questions concerning the globular star clusters—their structure, relationships, stellar content—I realized that we were relatively more ignorant about them than when I had started my investigation. I had added more to the unknown than to the known. A score of technical papers had been written, but I could not catch up with the unfolding scheme. I found problems we had not known were in existence. Even now, many years later, I remain chagrined that we are still ignorant, without even good leading hypotheses, concerning the origin, dynamics, and destiny of these great stellar systems. It was something of a jolt to discover "how much the unknown transcends the what we know" (in Longfellow's words) and to realize that it will ever be so, unless there should come favorable mutations in the human intellect toward greater wisdom and comprehension. With our present neural equipment we are not able to know everything about anything, and doubtless there are vast fields of the partly knowable that we do not even understand well enough to realize that we are ignorant about them.

It is all rather discouraging for an ambitious inquirer; that is, it is discouraging until he appreciates that what counts in the progress of the human mind is the research rather than the findings—the inquiring, the questioning, not the final reply. How suicidally dull it would be if we knew all the answers!

A BIOLOGICAL THROWBACK

The other special moment of discovery came to me one day while kneeling before the great god Biological Evolution. The kneeling was on a sandy lot at the corner of Lake Street and East Orange Grove in Pasadena, California. The altar before me was a hole in the ground. Out of the hole streamed the busy and beautiful members of a rich colony of the Harvester ant.

I had seen scores of these societies and had greatly admired their industry in harvesting and processing the wild barley. In this particular case I had been watching with admiration the valor of the colony in a hopeless combat with an invading group of Argentine ants. But what had mainly attracted my notice was something about this colony which was far more unusual.

There are at least 3,500 known species of ants, and practically all the species live in social organizations. Some of their societies are simple and primitive, others extraordinarily integrated—beyond the development of human society. But the ants were not always social animals. There was a time when the forebears of the ants were like flies and grasshoppers: everybody was fertile and everybody for himself—no central colonial establishment, no statism, all in completely free enterprise. Now the ants are highly organized in societies consisting of two major castes—the common worker ant (comprising the overwhelming majority), which is effectively sexless, and the small, aristocratic caste of fertile males and queens, which pass on the genetic inheritance of the species from one generation to the next. For the past 40 or 50 million years, the worker and fertile ants have lived in colonies, totally dependent on the whole community for food and shelter. Society had been discovered, adopted, and developed millions of years before men tried it.

In the pre-societal days (probably pretty far back in the Mesozoic Era, some hundred million years ago or more), the forerunners of the ants all had wings—two pairs of wings—like the wasps, whose ancient ancestors they probably had in common. But in the last 40 or 50 million years the worker ant has been wingless. And this brings me to that curious colony at the corner of Lake Street and East Orange Grove.

On the backs of many of the worker ants in the colony I had noticed little spots or knots, little feathery protuberances. This was a surprise. The tidy and intense worker ants are clean, forever primping and polishing their chitinous surfaces. There should be no spots or stains!

I had sent some specimens from the nest to the leading American authority on ants, William Morton Wheeler of Harvard University. Dr. Wheeler had verified my identification of the species (*Pogonomyrmex californicus*), and as for the spots on the backs of some of the specimens—those tiny nodules were vestiges of wings! The ants were, in fact, pterergates—a pretty name derived from the Greek words for wings and workers.

Worker ants with indications of wings? This was indeed a rarity. At that time in the myrmecological collections of the world only six pterergates were known—three collected from New York (Bronxville), one from England, one from Belgium, and one from Cuernavaca in Mexico. Those six specimens represented four different species of ants.

Now, kneeling over the nest at the Pasadena street-corner, I was looking at more pterergates than had been reported by ant men in all their observations the world over. I examined the ants closely as they emerged from their hole. On many of them, the nodules on the mesothorax were not merely faint vestiges but actually miniature wings, with veining, supporting ribs, and all that makes up the mature ant wing, such as the queen mother possesses temporarily and uses in her nuptial flight. A few of the worker ants were equipped with all four wings—miniature, useless little wings—and as they busied themselves around the mouth of the nest, they looked like jolly little four-winged cherubim.

I counted the winged workers in that colony of some 1,500 ants. Seven hundred and forty pterergates was my final census—a strange nest indeed, with about half the population queer! Other nests of Harvester ants in the same neighborhood had no pterergates at all. And the pterergates in this nest were entirely normal in all other respects—body structure, work assignments, and so on. They were distinguished from ordinary Harvester ants only by this one genetic oddity, inherited from their queen.

What was so remarkable about this observation of worker ants with functionally useless little wings? Nothing, perhaps, if one looks at it merely as a genetic curiosity. But it struck me at once as a throwback to the Cretaceous period of the Mesozoic Era—a bridging back from the present through some ten million generations of mother-queens of *Pogonomyrmex californicus*. On my knees before this biotic altar I was suddenly in the age of the mighty reptiles. Dinosaurs roamed the swamps in the time represented by these specimens, when the ants were gradually yielding their independence as individuals, abandoning their ability to fly, and adopting certain colonial advantages and restrictions. Before me was a living fossil society.

An occasional reversion of a single individual to a primitive type might pass as just a biological curiosity—a sort of freak or monster in the myrmecological household. But the hundreds of pterergates in this one nest pointed back to our lowly origins, social as well as anatomical. (In using the word "our" I have in mind all of us social animals.) We could not simply say that something had gone wrong with an egg and produced a freak. It was more than that; it suggested a genetic remnant of social primitivism. Here was direct evidence of our linkage with the geological past—a kind of recapitulation of an early phase of social development, much as the human fetus recapitulates the evolution of the human vertebrate. To me it was a look at an embryonic stage of a highly developed society. It incited, of course, analogical thinking. Here was a social throwback after ten million generations, and man's society has existed for a few hundred generations at most!

If fate and the bellicose Argentine ants had permitted the survival of that nest of Pogonomyrmex ants, and if the operation of natural selection had permitted the reestablishment of winged workers, one can imagine that this ant society, after 50 million years of social habits, might have tended back toward the non-social family rites of the Mesozoic. But that is mere fancy and bears little on my moment of realization that society—whether human or invertebrate—is still tied to the past, still infected with the manners of geologically ancient times.

It also brought a humbling realization of the brevity of man's experience and the human animal's small place in time. I might not have been so bemused by this thought if I had been a more diligent reader of the philosophies of past and present. Sir Isaac Watts put it neatly in a hymn:

> *Great God! how infinite art thou!*
> *What worthless worms are we!*

That sounds humble enough, until one explores the biological antiquity of worms, their store of instincts, and their marvelously intricate structure; then he is likely to agree with my friend Henry Norris Russell: "How frightfully complimentary to man!"

The globular clusters had helped to locate man and his works in the space dimension. The social Harvester ants provided, for me at least, an orientation in time, and a vantage point from which to view the current evolutionary troubles of our multi-nation society.

Our study of the distribution of stars and their time scales, and study of the paleontological records, tends to promote calmness with respect to current terrestrial matters. It also tends to enhance one's respect for the overall evolutionary trends, which include the birth and development of atoms and galaxies, the origin and rise of animal societies on this peripheral planet, and the struggle of the human intellect to comprehend and take a little part in what is going on.

We shall next examine the evidence that the inorganic universe is a dynamic affair, rich and widely spread, with its biology and evolving atoms building up the organization of energy, and its radiating stars running it down.

2

A Bird's Eye View
of Our Galaxy

Let us take a bird's-eye view of our own galaxy. The bird whose eye we would use to get a proper outside look must be far more distant than any we know. We cannot use Cygnus the Swan, which wings in full flight along the northern Milky Way, nor Aquila the Eagle, nor the big-billed Toucan, nor the Flamingo, the Phoenix, the Goose, the Bird of Paradise, nor Corvus the Crow. All these constellation birds are composed of bright stars well within the Milky Way system.

What we need is an observation post a few million light-years distant. It would be pretty satisfactory to settle our bird comfortably in the outer haze of stars of the Andromeda Nebula. If the Andromedan bird is a contemporary of ours, it will be looking at our system in the light of 20,000 cen-

15

turies ago. It has been that long since our sun's light began its journey to the retina of the all-comprehending but quite imaginary bird now surveying us from the Andromeda galaxy.

Such a temporal disparity, two million years, is of no particular moment in our considerations of the galaxies; short-term enterprises like our current western civilization, or even the whole history of mankind, can be neglected as too momentary, too fleeting, for a clear recording in the cosmic panorama.

It is well known that the Milky Way star system is a much flattened organization and that the sun and planets are well inside. This interpretation of the Milky Way was pointed out two centuries ago by Thomas Wright, a pioneer "bird's-eye viewer" of Durham, England. He saw that the hypothesis of a flattened stellar system with the earth near the central plane would satisfactorily explain the Milky Way band of starlight as a phenomenon of projection.* Our hypothetical observer in Andromeda would see our flattened, wheel-shaped system not from the direction of its rim, nor from the direction of its axis, but from an intermediate position. It would appear in projection, therefore, as an elongated object, with the axes of the rough ellipse in the ratio of about three to one. There would be a conspicuous globular nucleus of naked-eye brightness.

We are certain now that our galaxy is a great openwork spiral system of stars, perhaps not much unlike the system

---

* For an account of the early cosmic interpretations by Emanuel Swedenborg, Thomas Wright, and Immanuel Kant, see the highly interesting report by F. A. Paneth, *The Observatory*, pp. 71 ff., June 1941; also H. Shapley's "Immanuel Kant, 1724–1924," Chapter 5, Yale University Press, 1925, E. C. Wilm, ed.

Messier 83 as we see it, but in linear measure it may be much larger. It has taken a long time to get conclusive evidence on the structure of our own system. We are badly located for seeing it. There are obvious difficulties with residing inside. The meadow violet, no matter how bold and sensitive, is at a disadvantage in meadow topography compared with the bird hovering above. Yes, we are awkwardly placed.

For more than a hundred years astronomers have struggled with the problems of the structure of the galaxy. There have been many poorly informed speculators, but also some gifted and systematic observers. Sir William Herschel dominated this field in the early part of the nineteenth century. His surveys of star clusters and nebulae, his measures of brightness and positions of various celestial objects, his interpretations of the accumulating material were so important that he is appropriately considered the founder of sidereal astronomy. Before Herschel, the astronomical emphasis had been on comets and planets, on the positions and motions of nearby stars, and on the laws governing these motions. The telescopes and the wisdom of scientists had focused essentially on solar-system astronomy. But when this German-Anglican organist of Bath devised more powerful instruments, astronomy turned outward to interstellar space.

Sir William Herschel was considerably baffled by the problems of the structure of the galaxy and by the relation of clusters and nebulae to the Milky Way. His successors made many notable contributions, photometric and spectroscopic, to knowledge of the nature of stars and nebulae, yet the large cosmic problems remained baffling. But eventually increases in the strength of telescopes and the accumulation of many kinds of observations reduced the puzzlement about the stellar neighbors of the sun and the nearer parts of the Milky Way. The concept that the spiral nebulae and their relatives were external galaxies, coordinate with our own Milky Way system, gradually became established. The dimensions of the galaxy and of the universe approached clarification, chiefly through the power of American telescopes and the vision of European and American theoreticians.

In clarifying some of the earlier puzzles, however, the astronomers only succeeded in opening vaster vistas for exploration, interpretation, and wonderment. The net gain has been considerable, thanks to ingenious solutions of the severe difficulties in astronomical observation. Something over a hundred years ago a distinguished scientist (not an astronomer) gloated a bit over his pronouncement that one thing would certainly remain forever unknown, namely, the chemical nature of the stars! It was not many years later that the spectroscope began to betray him. By 1941 Dr. Annie Cannon had classified more than a quarter of a million stars on the basis of the chemistry of their surfaces. Much is now known about the chemical constitution of a galaxy of a billion stars at a distance of ten million light-years. An elementary astronomical student can quickly learn, with the use of modern equipment, about the hydrogen, calcium, iron, magnesium, helium, carbon, and other elements in stars which have never actually been seen except through use of the photographic plate.

One moral of that short-sighted pronouncement about stellar chemistry is that it is not wise to be discouraged by difficulties arising from our isolation and awkward location in the galaxy. Eventually all the answers to all the reasonable questions you could now ask about Milky Way structure may be known. And of course we will then be wise enough to ask other "unanswerable" questions. Here are some of the current questions, and, for a few, preliminary answers.

ITS FORM AND DIMENSIONS

1. Are the sun and its planets in the middle of our discoidal galaxy? They certainly are not, as the preceding chapter reports in detail. There are now many lines of evidence which indicate that the center is far away in the direction of the place where the constellations of Sagittarius, Ophiuchus, and Scorpio come together, 30 degrees or a little more south of the celestial equator in the thick of the bright star clouds along the Milky Way. There may be "subcenters" in other parts of the Milky Way—in far south Carina, for instance, and in Cygnus. But such conglomerations of stars appear only to be local structures within a great galaxy which has its massive nucleus in the Sagittarius direction.

2. Is this galaxy in motion as a unit? Yes, it certainly rotates on its axis. It rotates not as a solid wheel but more in the manner of our planetary system, in which the planets revolve around the sun at different speeds, those nearer the sun moving more rapidly and completing their "years" in shorter times than the remoter planets. We think we can definitely measure the speeds of stars revolving around the nucleus of our galaxy. The average speed in the sun's neighborhood is nearly 200 miles a second, and the present direction of our motion is toward the northern constellation of Cygnus.

3. How far are the sun and its neighboring stars from the axis of the galaxy's rotation? Ten kiloparsecs is the approximate answer: that is, something like 200 quadrillion miles, or 30-odd thousand light-years. For various reasons, that value

of ten kiloparsecs is not too certain, but it seems well established that the figure lies between eight and twelve kiloparsecs. The direction to the center is fixed with an uncertainty of only one or two degrees; this measurement was much easier to handle than the distance.

4. How large is the Milky Way system and how populous? Enormous in size and population. There is good evidence that the total population of stars is of the order of 200,000 million, but the evidence on overall dimensions is as yet inconclusive. Indeed, it is somewhat involved with definitions. For instance, how do we define the boundary of a galaxy? Is it at the distance from the axis to the farthest discoverable member of the system? Or is it at the place where the number of stars per cubic light-year has decreased to some specified small quantity? Or is it, for a spiral galaxy, at the limit to which a spiral arm can be traced photographically? Or is it the distance to which an escaping star can go before the gravitational hold-back is exceeded by the pull from some other galaxy?

The diameter of our galactic system in its plane is not less than 100,000 light-years, if all its recognizable stars are included. There is now good evidence that the wheel-shaped system is surrounded by a more or less spherical haze of stars, and some of the stars in the haze are 50,000 light-years above the plane of the Milky Way. Probably this haze extends even more distantly in the plane of the system and, therefore, the diameter of discoid plus haze considerably exceeds 100,000 light-years. But 90 per cent of all its stars are in the nucleus.

5. Why is it that we seem to be so baffled about the structure and dimensions of our own system, although we bravely go out to distances of 100 million light-years in our explora-

tions for other galaxies? What is so troublesome about measuring something that completely surrounds us and is near at hand?

That question finally brings out one feature of Milky Way structure which our bird in Andromeda could detect at a glance but which has taken us many years and much labor to discover and partly evaluate. This basic feature is the presence throughout the Milky Way, especially near the Milky Way plane, of dust and gas, scattered and in clouds, around the stars and in the spaces between them. In a bird's-eye view, this haze or smog would be clearly discernible, but we inside have the greatest difficulty in defining its extent and density. Consequently, we have found it hard to estimate accurately how much of a distant star's light it absorbs and to get an accurate measure of the star distance.

Gradually we are learning, through studies of colors and otherwise, how to make corrections for the interstellar absorption. It would not be difficult at all if the absorbing material were uniformly distributed. But the clouds of absorption are irregular patches and lanes. Presumably some of the greatest irregularities in our galaxy would be apparent to the Andromedan observer. Looking at other galaxies from our own bird's-eye position, we can easily see the dark lanes of dust and gas between their spiral arms.

In summary, our imaginary bird's-eye view of the Milky Way system shows that its main body of stars takes the form of a disk, probably surrounded by a thinly populated spheroidal haze of stars and dominated by a massive globular nucleus which contains a hundred billion stars and is some 30,000 light-years from the sun in an accurately measurable direction. Less certainly, the view discloses that our galaxy is a spiral, perhaps more open in structure than the somewhat

larger Andromeda galaxy; it is rotating at high speed, but even so, two million centuries or possibly more will be required for the sun and its neighbors to complete one circuit —to click off one cosmic year. Uncertainty remains as to the overall dimensions of our galaxy and of its stellar haze, and this uncertainty arises in part from the existence of light-absorbing, mostly nonluminous, interstellar material.

THE LOCAL CLOUD OF GALAXIES

If, for a more distant view of this part of the universe, we went off into space a hundred million light-years in a certain direction, the Andromeda nebula and our galactic system would look to us like a pair of galaxies, separated by only a few diameters. In the same field, apparently also a part of our local group of galaxies, would be the great spiral called Messier 33. A closer inspection from this distant point, and a careful measurement of distances, would show several fainter, smaller galaxies associated with these three large systems. Two of them would be the faint companions of the Andromeda galaxy—Messier 32 and NGC 205. Two others would be our own satellite-companions—the Large and Small Clouds of Magellan. And there would be visible other dwarf galaxies, two of them irregular in form, and two or more spheroidal.

The existence of this local cloud of galaxies, in which our system appears to be a dominating member, is now beyond question, but the census of its membership is not complete. All the known members are within a sphere of two million light-years' radius. Those unknown, or of uncertain membership, include systems wholly or partly concealed by the clouds of absorption near the Milky Way plane. The rating of the great globular clusters is also not yet wholly clear. A hundred globular clusters surround our galaxy. All of them appear to be subordinate members of our galactic system, but perhaps the larger ones, notably Omega Centauri and 47 Tucanae, should be ranked as dwarf galaxies on the edge of our system. In total luminosity and in mass they are comparable to NGC 205, the faint spheroidal galaxy in the Andromeda group.

Groups like our local "supergalaxy" occur elsewhere in metagalactic space. A dozen rich clusters are known, some of them with hundreds of members, and many scores of small groups similar to our own are already on record. One such is a group of objects in Fornax; there the brightest members are spheroidal, while in our group the brightest galaxies are spiral in form.

SUPERLUMINOUS STARS

On every expedition into remote regions of extragalactic space, it is necessary to equip ourselves with information on giant and supergiant stars. The reason is, obviously, that at a great distance ordinary stars are too dim to be recorded on our photographs; we can observe only the giants. It will be of interest to consider the following highly luminous stars and types of stars and see how they contribute to knowledge of the Metagalaxy:

1. Supernovae.
2. S Doradus.
3. Novae.
4. P-Cygni stars and others.

1. *Supernovae.* "The most energetic catastrophe in the history of the universe, unless it be the Creation itself," is how I would describe the great violence of radiation and motion that accompanies the career of a supernova. Simply defined, a supernova results when a star blows up. Whether the disaster is caused or encouraged by head-on collision with another star or with another something, or is caused by the collapse of the star's structure, with the consequent transformation of atomic mass into radiation, or whether it "just happens," we cannot yet say. More observational data are needed and are being obtained. The evidence of a supernova outburst is an unparalleled outpouring of light—a spurt of radiation sometimes equivalent to 50 million suns and more. The burst of radiation may last several days or weeks, quieting down slowly as the months go by. What remains after the flare-up? Perhaps a dense subdwarf star (the collapsed core of the original star); perhaps a rapidly expanding nebula; perhaps just dust and ashes, the region filling up with the dying glow of a radiant moment.

Dr. Fritz Zwicky of the California Institute of Technology has been a leader in the discovery of supernovae and in speculations concerning them. He thinks that neutrons and neutrinos may play an important part in the supernova phenomenon. Certainly supernovae play a significant part in the history of the universe. They are not too uncommon. About 40 were on record before 1940. Three of them appeared long ago in our own galactic system. One theory of the origin of cosmic rays ties up these energetic particles with the violence of the supernova.

The most remote individual stars yet photographed are supernovae in galaxies tens of millions of light-years distant. When more data are obtained, we shall be able to see whether supernovae can be used as practical criteria of distance. At present there seems to be too much variation in the intrinsic luminosities of supernovae at maximum light to make them useful for distance measurement in the Metagalaxy.

Long before supernovae were recognized as stellar disasters, and long before there was the faintest notion of their enormous violence as celestial phenomena, they played a very important part in astronomical development and in knowledge of the universe. For it happens that two brilliant new stars which appeared suddenly in 1572 and 1604 were important in the inspiration of two of the great astronomers of all time —Tycho Brahe, the Dane, and Johannes Kepler, the German. Now we know that these stellar outbursts in Cassiopeia (Tycho's star) and in Ophiuchus (Kepler's *stella nova*) were most probably supernovae. Both stars rose to a brightness in the sky comparable with that of the brightest planet; both brightened explosively by about 15 magnitudes—more than a millionfold increase of brightness.

A third supernova of our galactic system was recorded by Japanese and Chinese astrologers in 1054. That phenomenon was the parent of the present well-known Crab Nebula, which is still rapidly expanding as a result of the eleventh-century disaster—eleventh century in our records, but probably 5,000 years earlier on the cosmic clock, for it took that long for their light to reach us.

2. *The Supergiant S Doradus.* The distinction of holding, temporarily at least, top place as a luminous star has been the lot of an object at the edge of one of the open clusters in the Large Magellanic Cloud. It is a variable star with average luminosity a million times that of the sun. It is somewhat exceeded in radiation output by some supernovae, but they

do not last, whereas S Doradus has been continuously radiating for at least the past half century, pouring out more than 200 trillion tons of radiation per minute. It must have enormous resources to persist at such high luminosity. Is it, perhaps, some very slow type of supernova? The spectrum of the star is of the rare P-Cygni type, which is indicative of unusually hot surface conditions. Its life will therefore be short, on the cosmic time scale. Recent photographs with Harvard's large southern reflector have shown that stars nearly as bright as S Doradus are clustered around it, but unfortunately all of them are difficult to study: notwithstanding their great intrinsic luminosities, the intervening distance of 160,000 light-years dims the light so much that even our large telescopes can hardly make detailed analyses of them. In our own neighborhood, no star is one-tenth as luminous as S Doradus.

3. *Ordinary Novae.* Several times a year, if we pay close attention, we find new stars in our own galactic system, especially in the direction toward the galactic center in Sagittarius. We know from sampling that there must be many of these events that we do not see because they occur during daylight or strong moonlight or on cloudy nights, or simply because no one was watching at the right time and place. These star flare-ups, or ordinary novae, behave somewhat like supernovae. But the phenomenon is much less violent, and a whole star is not sacrificed by the outburst. It is likely that an ordinary nova represents an explosive eruption of only the outer portion of a star. There is some evidence that before their explosions the ordinary novae are slightly subnormal stars of the ordinary spectral types. Perhaps this subnormality is at the bottom of the trigger action that sets them off.

Whatever the cause, novation must be recorded as an interesting phenomenon, and one that probably is important in the general history of stars. In our own galaxy, and in the neighboring Andromeda galaxy, these common novae appear so frequently that when we think back over the past billions of years that the earth's crust has existed, we conclude that very many stars have blown up—a large proportion of them! Novation is so common, and time has been so long, that perhaps every star either has blown up once already or will explode during the next billion years. Sidereal evolution by way of the nova outburst may be a major phenomenon in the universe.

Evidence is accruing that novation is a repetitive phenomenon. Four or five stars, our records show, have been novae more than once, and two of them three times since 1860. If this be the true situation—that is, only stars of peculiar character become novae and most stars do not explode—we may remain even more at ease with respect to the immediate future of our sun. Its character is good and normal. We like to believe that the sun will remain only slightly variable (in the sunspot period), and will also remain undisturbed by interstellar dust clouds, unsusceptible to nova-inciting disturbance—at least for the next thousand years while the astronomers are "solving" the universe. A novalike change in the sun would promptly wipe biology off the earth, if it did not erase the planet altogether.

At maximum an ordinary nova is a supergiant star, more than 10,000 times as luminous as the sun but scarcely 1 per cent as radiant as the average supernova. When ordinary novae appear in external galaxies they can be used as distance indicators, because at maximum brightness the ordinary nova rises always to about the same candlepower. Comparing the apparent brightness with the real brightness, the distance in light-years can readily be computed. Next to the Cepheid variables, novae are the best criteria for estimating distances of galaxies, providing enough are found in any given system to stabilize the statistics. Only for the nearer galaxies, however, can the common novae be identified. For distant galaxies we must use the uncertain and infrequent supernovae.

4. *Some Other Supergiants.* Two or three magnitudes fainter than the brilliant S Doradus in the Large Magellanic Cloud is a type of star with the same peculiar spectrum—the so-called P-Cygni class. There is evidence, not quite conclusive, that these stars are related to the novae, but they differ in that they retain steadily their high luminosities instead of fading away after the impulsive outburst. In addition to these bluish hot stars, we find in the Magellanic Clouds supergiant red stars, almost as bright. Some of them are variable, and some, indeed, are long-period Cepheid variables, 10,000 times as bright as the sun. Many resemble the famous red giants of our neighborhood, Antares and Betelgeuse. A few greatly exceed our local red supergiants in volume as well as in radiation output. They appear to be ten million times the volume of the sun. These preposterous dimensions are estimated from their known distances (*i.e.,* the distances of the Magellanic Clouds), from their total candlepowers, and from their spectra, which indicate that their efficiency of radiation is low. In order to give out as much radiation as they do, they must have an exceedingly large surface. The bluish S Doradus, on the other hand, which is a more efficient radiator, is much smaller and denser than the Clouds' Antares-like red supergiants.

The future of research on galaxies probably depends not so much on the size of telescopes as on the speed and resolving power of photographic plates and on the effectiveness of other radiation-registering devices. But even without better facilities than those at present available, astronomers have plenty to do in galactic research, for within reach are a billion individual stars in our own galaxy, and at least ten million other galaxies.

3

---

*Evolution in
the Expanding Universe*

A century ago Charles Darwin's *Origin of Species* was published, and as a consequence our concept of man forthwith underwent a major mutation. We have appropriately celebrated Darwin and his courageous collaborators, and in so doing we have extended his basic growth principle (evolution) far beyond the point of emphasis of a century ago, when only the origins and development of plant species and of animal species were explored. We now go much farther back than Darwin and the paleontologists went. Also we now look timidly forward. Along with Robert Burns we may say to the panicked mouse that she is fortunate compared with the human plowman, for

30

The present only touches thee:
But, och! I backward cast my ee
On prospects drear!
An' forward, tho' I canna see,
I guess an' fear!

Let us cast our ee backward as far as we can before we look and guess timidly forward.

Both for scholars and for laymen the term evolution generally incites only biological thoughts—of apes that resemble humans, dogs that evolve from ancestral wolves, hybrid corn that shames the primitive grain from which it developed. But evolution is much broader than biological concepts and operations, as the following discussion will show.

The sun shines. The obviousness of that fact is exceeded only by the statement's importance. For therein lies a complete answer to those who deny, or at least question, on the grounds of mistaken theological orthodoxy, the occurrence of any kind of evolution.

There is nothing miraculous in sunshine. It represents the transfer across space of energy that is produced by atomic activities at the surface of a star. A lighted match is analogous. The match and the sun both send out to surrounding cooler environments their visible and invisible radiations. The energy stored in the molecules of the match and in the atoms of the sun flows outward from the hot sources, and by its leaving the masses are reduced. Our sun grows less in mass second by second, hour by hour, year by year, simply because it shines. Inevitably, and concurrently with the change of mass, the volume or density or both must also change; through radiating, therefore, the sun evolves, and does so irreversibly. Sunshine produces solar evolution, and the rate of change in mass is measured by the basic principle tied up in Einstein's $M = E/c^2$ formula.

By extension of the argument, starshine indicates that the billions of radiating stars also evolve. For when a star shines away some of its stored-up energy E, and thereby losses mass M, there occurs of necessity change in other, related physical properties. Eventually the alterations in mass, temperature, size, and density will be sufficient to affect measurably the amount of radiation. And in a long, long time the changes will affect the biological situations on whatever life-bearing planets there may be in the star's family of dependents.

The foregoing preliminary argument sets the stage for inquiries about various facets of inorganic evolution. For example, do nebulae evolve? And star clusters? And even the mighty galaxies? And how about comets? Or, to get closer to mankind, how about the evolution of and on planets, on one in particular? Have the seas and mountains of this planet's crust changed with time? Have the chemistries of the oceans and soils also changed?

The deepest of all inquiries for the non-biological evolutionist are questions concerning the evolution of the atoms of which all matter is composed, and, at the other extreme of size, the origin, growth, and destiny of the total universe.

MAN'S INHERENT INCOMPETENCE

Many of these questions are beyond our present knowing, perhaps beyond the knowable. Before we undertake to present some partial answers, it might be well to intimate why we cannot hope to present the full and final responses.

Briefly, it is because we are dumb. Congenitally dumb, and there is not much we can do about it except play spiritedly in the noble game of "Approach." We sometimes conceal our failure to attain full knowledge behind the neat phrase that it is after all better to search than to find. And sometimes we seek to justify our continuous, nervous efforts to find answers by the argument that it is better to go as far as we can than to sit on our hands; better to grope hopefully, approach truth bravely, even with our poor equipment for knowing, than to remain ignorantly idle, offering false panaceas, such as the claim that all questions can be amply answered through reliance on supernatural deity.

My simple, perhaps too simple, diagnosis of our failure to comprehend the universe is that we have been and still are bedeviled by a natural and persisting anthropocentrism. Correctives for our vanities are provided by modern science, but we suffer relapses and return to believing that we are somehow important and supremely powerful and understanding. Of course we are not.* We have learned that fact slowly, and accepted it but partially.

Two or three millennia ago, when early man began to explore and grope for answers to astronomical puzzles, the primeval human vanity and anthropocentric philosophy had to give way to geocentrism. That earth-center theory was a bit complicated, and eventually the simpler sun-centered concept (heliocentrism) took over. It was simpler for the sincere scholar, though perhaps not simple for the unthinking man, wrapped up in his self-esteem. There was even a bit of resistance on the part of the thoughtful, because change naturally incites resistance. For example, in its early days Harvard College stood by the geocentric interpretation for

---

* Salvador Dali dissents: "The universe is a slight thing compared with the amplitude of a brow painted by Raphael."

more than a century after the appearance of De Revolutionibus Orbium Coelestium.

The Copernican heliocentric cosmogony, as a successor of geocentrism, prevailed for more than three centuries and widened its range. The sun came to be considered central not only in its own planetary family but also in the whole world of stars. Central, but scarcely a ruling body, for the early telescopes had revealed millions of stars, and there was no good evidence that they were relatively small, or weak, or easily manageable. Admittedly the sun might not control the stellar universe, but the presumed central position of the sun and its planets supported man's claim to some vague cosmic pre-eminence.

The heliocentric hypothesis still stands firm so far as the local planets are concerned. But in 1917 the place of the sun with respect to the trillions of stars in the Milky Way and outside came under closer scrutiny. The powerful photographic telescopes were rapidly piling up revelations about this overall system of stars and nebulae. In the preceding decades, researches had suggested to a few that the sun was not exactly dead-center, but still it seemed to occupy the central position in the Milky Way, for its millions of stars formed a continuous circular band of light around us. Moreover, the numbers of stars were found to fall off with distance in nearly all directions, thus further supporting the suggestion of a central position for the sun and its planets.

Then came suspicions. When we learned how to estimate their distances, we found that the globular star clusters were concentrated in and around the southern Milky Way star clouds; novae (exploding stars) were likewise more frequent in southern Sagittarius, and so were bright nebulosities, superluminous variable stars, and star clouds.

These researches ended, after a few brief struggles with a

few cautious conservatives, in the establishment of the "galactocentric" hypothesis, as I have explained in Chapter 1. The sun is no longer thought to be in a central position. Rather, the center of the Milky Way galaxy is now known to be some 30,000 light-years distant.

The displacement of the sun and earth from positional importance, the sudden relegating of man to the edge of one ordinary galaxy in an explorable universe of billions of galaxies—that humiliating (or inspiring) development is or should be the death knell of anthropocentrism. It should incite orienting thoughts by modern philosophers and theologians, and perhaps it has and will.

Many an ancient philosopher, on the basis of relatively little knowledge of the universe, urged humility as appropriate for man. A century ago Charles Darwin and his cooperators, especially Thomas H. Huxley, presented a strong case for biological humility. The further orienting of man goes on steadily in these days of feverish scientific inquiry. Physically we are minimized. But that should not seriously disturb us, deflate our spirit, if we look at the situation objectively. All the new revelations should promote our respect for the universe and our pride in the human mind. Would that the mind were more powerful, more penetrating, more free of delusions, free of silly hopes and prejudices.

On man's further orientation in recent years I shall presently comment. But first a sort of apologetic explanation of our seeming dumbness.

OUR SURVIVAL EQUIPMENT

The term "dumb" is used relatively, of course. We do pretty well with what we have. So do the other organisms. Our sense organs and our astonishing forebrain have developed through serving the immediate interests of the three S's—survival, sex, and shelter—the third in a way being a part of the first. Our kit of survival tools was not equipped by Nature in the interest of abstract thought, or for the unrolling of cosmic theory, or for the holding of scientific conferences. Survival struggles, not philosophical hypotheses, led us out of the ancient jungles. For the survival of the individual, of the family, and especially of the species, we became clever, a few millenia ago, with our hands, with our game-catching tricks, with our sound-making apparatus.

These natural abilities obviously sufficed for our survival as primates. Therefore, from an animal point of view, the subsequent human cultures and art-filled civilizations are useless extras; they must look like abortions on the evolving stream of life. I should like to point out, however, to the turtles, crinoids, conifers, and similar biological successes, that the social and physical gadgets devised by human civilizations have up to now assisted very well in spreading the species, and that is one of the evolutionary goals. Assisted up to now, yes; beyond now, question mark!

Many fringe benefits accrued to the civilized human species after we acquired the bonus of idleness as a by-product of our easy and wide success in obtaining food and shelter. We have had time to fiddle around with religion first of all, then with arithmetic, with astrological brain-washing, rhetoric, and the like.

If survival of the individual and of our species had depended from the beginning upon deep reasoning and close attention to logical methodology, either we would have failed and long since attained the oblivion stored in mammalian fossils, or we would have developed our rational intellect a million years or so earlier than we did. If such development of reasoning had been required and achieved so long ago, the human mind might not still be in the rather confused and deplorable condition in which we now find it.

Eat, procreate, live it up!—that was the original program for the primates as it is now for our colleagues throughout the animal and vegetable kingdoms. Our human ancestors successfully carried it through, and after many a close escape here we are—after a couple of billion years of competitive terrestrial biology, here we are assessing the foibles and potentials of a few animal species, especially of man. In our anthropocentric eagerness, the Cosmos is almost entirely forgotten.

DOES LIFE EXIST ELSEWHERE?

Centuries ago, when the other known planets had been put in their correct places by terrestrial astronomers and some of them had been recognized as comparable to the Earth, speculators began to imagine the existence of planetary biology other than our own. Mars, for instance, was peopled with human life. This was all juicy meat for the fiction writers. The non-fictionists, to be sure, granted the possibility of low life on Mars—but life only of a vegetable sort, and not succulent vegetables at that. Martian algae and fungi were admitted as a possibility by those who measure and calculate about conditions on that cold, dry, thin-aired body.

In the past few decades, the picture has changed, not concerning the low-life prospects on Mars, but with regard to planets and life elsewhere. Several new scientific developments have joined in creating the new outlook. Four of them are (1) the discovery that the solar system is not at the center of the galaxy, as we had thought; (2) the new bio-

chemical researches on macromolecules; (3) the discovery
and measurement of the expanding universe, and (4) the
census of galaxies. Let us briefly review each of these discoveries.

1. The globular star clusters first contributed to the locating of the sun and its planets near the perimeter of our galaxy and showed it to be an immense system of some hundred thousand million stars. Stellar counts, nebular distribu-
tions, stellar dynamics, and more recently radio astronomy
have confirmed beyond undoing the peripheral position of
the solar family. When spectrum analysis showed that the
sun is a typical star, with no outstanding qualities except
that is it our star, we began to ask seriously and scientifically
whether we of the earth are the only living things in the universe or merely the local sample of what creation and evolution have done and can do.

2. In the study of biological evolution several important
advances have recently been made in the fields of photo-
synthetic research, virology, microbiology, and chemical bio-
genesis. From these researches it now seems clear that the
origin of life, however life is defined, is an inevitable step in
the gas and liquid evolution on a star-illuminated planet's
surface when the chemical, physical, and climatic conditions
are right—and the range of rightness can be wide, with considerable tolerance in temperatures, atmospheric pressures,
and the chemical constitution of air and water.

3. In the 1920's astronomers discovered a redward shift in
the light coming from many external galaxies, and it is now
all but universally accepted that this means that the huge
stellar systems are moving rapidly away in space. Nearly a
thousand of these difficult objects have been measured for
speed in the line of sight (radial velocity). In all directions

the same result appears—the more distant the galaxy, the greater its speed of recession from the earthbound observers, and for hypothetical observers in other galaxies the same phenomenon must prevail. Unquestionably the universe is expanding; the galaxies are scattering. Where are they going? That question is premature. Where did they come from? To that question we have at least a tentative answer: namely, they came out of some more concentrated state of affairs. For if the galaxies are now scattering, the system of them (which we may call the Metagalaxy or the Material Universe) was smaller yesterday—and last year, and much smaller a million years ago.

4. The large telescopes have in recent years confirmed the earlier suspicion that the number of stars must be reckoned in what is commonly called "astronomical figures." From sample star counts, and from measures of the star motions resulting from gravitational attraction throughout our galaxy, we conclude that the stars in our own system total more than 10^{11} equivalent suns. (Many of the stars are bigger and brighter than our sun, but a majority are of lesser size and light.)

IMPLICATIONS OF THE EXPANSION

All the evidence, in the light of present knowledge, indicates that a few thousand million years ago the stars and galaxies that we now observe were densely crowded together. (We need not go as far as accepting literally Canon Lemaître's single Primitive Atom that contained the whole mass of the universe.) In the early crowding, things happened that cannot happen now—namely, the *frequent* colliding and disrupting of stars, whether they were in the same shape and size as now or were in a proto-star state. These collisions were planet makers—both planet makers and planet disrupters.

Doubtless it was a lively time in the cosmos when our present multimillions of stars were a-borning in a medium that was rich in comets, disrupted stars, and planets, and rich also in interstellar clouds of gas and dust. Such confusion cannot easily occur now. Our times are relatively quiet; our spatial environment is thinly populated; our own sun and planets move around the galactic center in a calm 200-million-year cycle. During its past ten or fifteen revolutions the sun has fed without interruption the plants and animals on its No. 3 planet, little disturbed by the wild turbulence that prevailed in the early days.

The point of my excursion into cosmic genealogy is to emphasize the very high probability that millions of planetary births have occurred in our galaxy, and trillions in the other galaxies. If we seek some origin for planetary systems other than the inevitable catastrophes of the crowded early days, such for instance as the presently favored neo-Kant-Laplacian shrinking-nebula hypothesis, the birth of planets is even more common than supposed above. A planetary family would probably be the fate and fortune of all stars except those in dense associations, such as double stars and clusters, where perturbations would oust planet-making material.

Other galaxies are like ours in composition—stars, gas, and dust. With the naked eye we can see three or four external galaxies. Small telescopes dimly show a thousand; the larger instruments, used photographically, reveal millions, and no limit. About a million galaxies are on the Harvard photographs; we have measured nearly half for position, brightness, and type. Some of the Californian and South African telescopes go deeper. There are too many galaxies for full measure and analysis. We must work with samples. Sampling indicates that more than a billion are within our present telescopic reach, which extends well beyond a billion light-years.

Why present these dizzy numbers? To emphasize the abundance of stars, and its meaning to biological evolution. I would place the number of stars at more than 10^{20}. These hundred thousand million billion stars are available for the maintenance of life on whatever planets there may be around them. All are radiating the kind of energy needed for photosynthesis and for animal and plant metabolism. Twenty per cent of them are essentially identical with our sun in size, luminosity, and chemistry.

4

On the Evolution of Atoms, Stars, and Galaxies

To present the arguments for *inorganic* evolution in the light of current thought—I plead inability to give a durable account because of today's rapid developments in observation and interpretation, and because of the fragility of a number of the prevailing hypotheses. I shall simply review the trends in speculation on evolution for each of the most important classes in the material universe: the chemical elements, the stars and planets, the galaxies, and the material universe itself.

THE CREATION

Concerning the origin of the universe, two incomplete and not very satisfactory hypotheses have been seriously proposed and explored. In their present development one theory can be identified by associating it with the names of Georges Lemaître and George Gamow, and the other, with Hermann Bondi, Thomas Gold, and Fred Hoyle.

In dealing with such ancient, complicated, and mysterious matters as the origin of the universe, we are hardly concerning ourselves with science in *sensu strictu*. The subject is stained with metaphysics, religion, and mental aberrations.

To put it briefly, Canon Lemaître and his followers (there are not many of them) postulate an all-inclusive Primeval Atom, the radioactive bursting of which, some ten billion years ago, was the beginning of all material things. It is suggested that time and space also first appeared when the burst of the Primeval Atom inaugurated the expanding material universe. Immediately after the burst (Creation!) the now well-known natural laws took complete charge, and what is now observed in the macrocosmos and the microcosmos has been the *natural* development of the universe. The natural operations include (1) the observed scattering of the galaxies as a consequence of cosmic repulsion overriding gravitation, and (2) the creation of all the chemical atoms out of quanta of energy and out of the proton-electron-neutron-meson basic corpuscles.

The explosive creation hypothesis, without considerable refinement and protection by subhypotheses, gets into trouble with certain observations and with some theory. For example, many stars are much too young to have been born in the original outburst, though we can, of course, propose subsequent secondary bursts.

As to the alternate hypothesis, the proposers and their followers (and again we note that they are not numerous) solve the problem of the original creation by saying that there never was an original creation. The universe we know, according to this hypothesis, had no beginning and presumably will have no end; it is in a "steady state," and although there are numerous small-scale and localized regressions and progressions (evolution), the universe as a whole does not continuously progress or regress.

This second interpretation also is not wholly satisfactory, and it, too, may perish under the onslaught of observational data. So far it has survived, but in a few years it may be of historical interest only. Currently one of its difficulties is with the preliminary evidence that the universe is now expanding less rapidly than a billion years ago. This evidence from Palomar's Hale telescope suggests a "pulsating" universe—one that alternately expands and contracts. If the indication of a slowing down of expansion stands up under further observation and calculation, the steady-state hypothesis may be withdrawn by its proposers, or drastically modified.

We appear, therefore, to be rather helpless with regard to explaining the origin of the universe. But once it is set going, we can do a little better at interpretation. Accepting the strong evidence of an expansion from a denser conglomeration of matter, we can say that the speed of scattering is a linear or nearly linear function of the distance from the observer, and the size of the Metagalaxy is a function of time. The rate is still under investigation. The temporarily accepted expansion speed at a million light-years distance is only some 20 miles a second, but at a hundred million light-years' distance it is 2,000 miles a second, and at a billion light-years, 20,000.

Is space infinite? Can the recession of galaxies exceed 186,000 miles a second—the velocity of light? Those questions call for extrapolations too large to make our guesses dependable. But advances in theory and observation should in a few years make the guessing less wild. Already the various theoretical cosmogonists give confident answers to cosmogonical questions; the answers, however, are rarely in agreement.

With bold advances in cosmogony we may in the future hear less of a Creator and more of such things as "antimatter," "mirror worlds," and "closed space-time." Finality, however, may always elude us. That the whole universe evolves can be our reasonable deduction, but just why it evolves, or from where, or where to—the answers to those questions may be among the Unknowables.

THE HIGHER ALCHEMY IN STARS

The many kinds of atoms that constitute living and inanimate matter show no evidence at this time of growing in mass, no evidence of changing now from one atomic species to another, with the exception, of course, of the natural radioactivity of a few kinds of heavy atoms, such as uranium, thorium, and radium. But the natural radioactive change of radium into lead and helium, for example, is in itself a suggestion that under proper physical conditions other kinds of atoms might be transmuted. The medieval alchemists tried to change mercury into gold, but failed. They did not have at hand enough heat, or high enough atomic speeds. Our later cyclotrons have achieved such transmutation—established the higher alchemy.

The evidence that the masses of atoms of the heavy elements are integral multiples of the masses of lighter elements (when allowance is made for the isotope mixtures) naturally hints at the evolution of atoms—from simple to complex, from light to heavy. We agree that somewhere and at some time the organization of matter has evolved. If the evolution has not occurred on earth or in it, where has it occurred? And if not now, when?

There are those who believe, or at least suggest, that the birth of all the elements from simple hydrogen beginnings occurred at the time of the hypothetical burst of the hypothetical primeval atom. There would have been energy enough at that time and place. Such a theory of the evolution of matter would indicate that the elements may be all essentially of the same age.

In the beginning was the Word, it has been piously recorded, and I might venture that modern astrophysics suggests that the Word was hydrogen gas. In the very beginning, we say, were hydrogen atoms; of course there must have been something antecedent, but we are not wise enough to know what. Whence came these atoms of hydrogen, these atoms, 20,000,000,000,000 (and 66 additional zeros) in number—atoms that we now believe have been forged into the material make-up of the universe? What preceded their appearance, if anything? That is perhaps a question for metaphysics. The origin of origins is beyond astronomy. It is perhaps beyond philosophy, in the realm of the to us Unknowable.

Ordinary physics and astronomy suggest that *if* several billions of our years ago we had all that hydrogen and the natural physical laws, what we now see would have followed without the intervention of miracles, and without supernatural intercession. Gravitation, radiation, and eventually photosynthesis, genetics, and so forth—with operators such as these and the widely dispersed hydrogen atoms, the universe of galaxies, stars, planets, life, and man would have emerged—nothing supernatural required.

A most amazing scheme of evolution of the chemical elements, of which all matter is made, has recently emerged, thanks to erudite studies in astrophysics and nuclear physics. The evolution of the whole series of elements is concerned, from hydrogen and helium (the lightest atoms) through carbon, oxygen, iron, and three score other middle-weight atoms, to lead, radium, and the devil atom, uranium.

The interiors of the stars provide the locale of the atom building. High temperatures are required. Here on earth, and in the earth, there are no atomic mutations—except the natural radioactive breakdown of radium and some others into lead, helium, calcium, and argon. Not even the most elemental mutation, $4\,H = 1\,He + radiation$, occurs naturally on the earth, for it maintains no natural temperature high enough for that operation. The same holds for the other planets. Nor is it hot enough on the surface of the sun for the hydrogen burning, nor on the surface of other stars, nor in the diffuse nebulosities from which stars apparently are born.

To start the fusion involving hydrogen, helium and the heavier elements, we need temperatures in excess of ten millions degrees absolute. In the middle of the sun, such temperatures prevail—hot enough for the hydrogen-into-helium reaction, but not hot enough for the "cooking" of the heavier elements—not hot enough for the further steps in the evolution of complex inanimate matter. How were these heavier elements born? They appear to be built out of hydrogen "blocks"; the common carbon atom is exactly twelve times the hydrogen atom in weight; iron, 56 times; uranium, 238 times.

Our question to the cosomographer is: How are these heavier atomic structures evolved from simple hydrogen and helium?

Calculations show that at about ten or twelve million degrees the hydrogen fuel in average stars (like our sun) is gradually transformed into helium ashes. At densities above a thousand grams per cubic centimeter, and temperatures of one or two hundred million degrees in the nuclei of giant stars, the helium is transformed (burned) into the main isotopes of carbon, oxygen, and neon. And at temperatures from two to five billion degrees the nuclei of atoms like iron and nickel would be made. In quiet, quasi-stable, giant stars, however, such temperatures are not normally reached, even at the tremendously compressed centers.

But when a star blows up (nova and supernova) there is heat enough. Suppose the sun blew up and became a nova. Every year there are a score or so of such disasters in our star-populated galaxy. Something goes wrong with the control of the energy output. A star in such trouble suddenly increases its size and brightness. It blows off its outer atmospheric shells.

If the sun erupted into a nova, its brightness would increase, probably in a single day, to five or ten thousand times normal. The internal temperature would rise toward 100 million degrees, and some of the helium atoms, which had been born more calmly out of hydrogen, would be violently transformed into heavier elements. The explosion would scatter these new elements into space, as well as the helium and unburned hydrogen. From this scattered material eventually new stars would be formed, as a result of gravitational contraction and radiation pressure. The new-born stars would radiate with a higher central temperature, because the heavier elements would be involved. Such stars could then start again their risky lives where thermostatic controls may fail to function and novation again ensue.

Ordinary novae are not competent to do the synthesis of the heaviest elements. Their central temperatures are not hot enough. But here another violent operation enters—the supernova.

In the year 1054 A.D., as we noted in Chapter 2, a dazzling new light appeared in the sky—a star-like radiator which apparently outshone all others. The oriental astrologers made a record of it. It was visible in the daytime for a week or more and visible at night for a couple of years, but then it faded away from the sky and from the memory of man. Centuries later, in the same position among the constellations, a faint, small nebulosity was noticed. It was named the Crab Nebula because of its fancy shape. This nebula was not much unlike other well-known nebulosities, such as the famed one in the Sword of Orion. But closer examination with the photographic and spectropic tools of the astronomer showed that it was expanding, and at such a steady rate that, counting backward, we can accurately date its origin. The nebula is indeed the product of the explosion recorded in 1054—an explosion that actually occurred some 4,000 years before the supernova was first seen. It took about 40 centuries for the light from the explosion to reach the earth. This explosion was not a simple blowing off of the star's upper atmosphere but essentially its complete annihilation. The temperatures involved in the explosion are what astrophysicists would look for—a temperature source hot enough to cook the heavier elements.

The exploding supernova serves not only as a billion-degree oven for forming heavy atoms but also as an explosive agent for returning atomic material to interstellar space for subsequent star building. Also, much material is returned to space through the leaking of matter at the turbulent surfaces of supergiant reddish stars whose surface gravity is so weak (because of size) that rapidly moving atoms cannot be retained.

In summary, the evolution of matter appears to be a synthesis inside the stars of the heavy atoms out of hydrogen, which is accepted as the primordial, abundant, and simple No. 1 chemical element.* The synthesizing agency is high temperature and the consequent intense radiation. The atoms that mutate from hydrogen into heavier species as a result of rising temperature reach iron as a goal of stability. In 10^x years hydrogen may approach exhaustion throughout the universe and iron rise to top abundance. (The exponent x is not small!)

Although the evolution of atoms is essentially a one-way building-up process, except for natural radioactivity, which breaks atoms down, a cyclic phenomenon is involved in stellar evolution. It consists of the continual gravitational forming of stars out of gas and dust, and the explosive transformation of unstable stars by supernovation back into dust and gas again.

The earliest stars must have been made almost wholly of hydrogen, with helium and perhaps a little of the oxygen group of elements appearing when the central temperatures were increased above 10 million degrees through the agency of gravitational compression. After a supernovation spreads some of the evolved star stuff into space again, "second generation" stars may form from this dust, which then contains

---

* For a full account of theories of the stellar synthesis of atoms, see article by Margaret and Geoffrey Burbidge in *Science*, August 22, 1958.

some of the heavier elements as well as hydrogen. In time, some of these second-generation stars, it is surmised, go through the supernova operation and still heavier elements are synthesized by the higher temperatures, and again dispersed in space. Another generation of stars then arises and so on. Our sun may be a third-generation star, for it contains all kinds of heavy atoms.

Perhaps the details of the foregoing mixture of brave speculation, intricate calculation, and sound interpretation are prematurely proposed. Nevertheless, the evolution of matter in stellar interiors appears to be a proper deduction from current theory and observation.

GALACTIC EVOLUTION

The evidence for inorganic evolution at the galaxy level is clear. We know that there are many kinds of galaxies. A gross classification would mention the ellipsoidal systems, the spirals, and irregular galaxies like the Clouds of Magellan. A finer classification divides the spheroidals into eight subclasses, the spirals also into eight subclasses, and the irregulars into several ill-defined categories. But all galaxies have one thing in common: they are composed of stars. There is much local clustering of giant stars in the open-armed spirals and in the irregular galaxies, and in them is also much interstellar gas and dust.

Finer classifications of galaxies, involving their spectra, the amount of included smog, characteristics of the spiral arms, etc., can be set up; actually one might propose a separate class for nearly every galaxy, because exact duplicates seem to be very rare. It is possible to arrange the galaxies in a continuous series, according either to form or to spectrum, and the existence of such a series immediately suggests evolution.

Three other indicators of the progressive evolution of galaxies can be cited.

The first is that, since galaxies are star-composed, and, as already noted, starshine itself is necessarily an indication of stellar evolution, so galaxy shine must mean galactic evolution.

The second is that, so far as we have been able to measure them, the galaxies are found to be rotating around their central axes or nuclei, and the rotational speeds vary with distance from the axis. The consequent shearing action smooths out the clustering and tends to dissolve the spiral arms (in our galaxy as well as others). Therefore, the direction of evolutionary progress, I believe, is from the irregular galaxies and open-armed spirals toward the close-armed spirals and spheroidals. This, of course, means an evolution of form on the galactic level, and we do not see it as reversible.

The third indicator of galactic evolution is that supergiant stars are numerous in the open-armed spirals, and practically absent from the spheroidals. Such supergiants radiate away their mass so rapidly that in a few million years they will disappear, not to return. That again means evolution in the structure of galaxies, as well as in their light and mass—an evolution from spiral toward spheroidal. There is, however, a possibility that the dying supergiants are replaced by other supergiant stars, newly born from the generally present gas and dust.

Although no one questions the assertion that galaxies, the great cosmic units of the universe, evolve, to visualize the nature of their evolution we need much fuller knowledge of the changes in form, light, and internal motion, as a function of time.

The Metagalaxy as a whole is expanding, but we know of thousands of clusters of galaxies where cosmic repulsion has not yet dissolved the local gravitational organization. As mentioned earlier, our own galaxy is in such a group, along with the Magellanic Clouds, the Andromeda triplet, and a few others, all of which are not more than two or three million light-years distant. These groups of galaxies undoubtedly evolve, perhaps by slow dispersion, but at what rate we cannot say.

STELLAR EVOLUTION

Finally, a few words on the evidence of stellar evolution. Here also we arc able to put practically all stars into various continuous series. For example, a *surface-temperature* series runs from about 3,000°C. to more than 30,000°C. —from cool reddish stars through yellow and greenish to hot bluish stars like the bright ones in Orion. In size a series runs from stars less than a tenth the volume of the sun to stars with a million times the sun's volume or more. In the *mean-density* series the variation is from the collapsed and degenerate white dwarfs, more than a thousand times the density of water, to the supergiant red stars, which are essentially vacua with mean densities only a millionth that of water. There is no question but that evolution, sometimes in strange ways, prevails along these three series.

It is our current belief, subject of course to modifications as the amount and strength of the evidence increases, that the white dwarfs, such as the companion of the bright star Sirius, are at the end of their careers—or rather, that they represent a major approach toward the extinction they may never quite reach.

The beginning of stars—that is, their birth out of radiation, dust, and gases—appears to be well represented by the lightless "globules" of matter in interstellar space. They can be detected only when they have bright diffuse nebulosity as a background. A few score of these photostars have been noted by Bart J. Bok and others. In diameter the globules are very large, dwarfing the greatest supergiant red stars. But gravitational contraction is inevitable, and eventually their dimensions will shrink, their interiors heat up, energy of radiation will flow to the surface, and a faint reddish glow will herald the arrival of a new light in the firmament.

The stars, especially those in crowded regions and those deep in nebulosity, are subject to various vicissitudes. Some blow off their outer atmospheres and become novae; some blow up completely (supernovae). Some lose matter disastrously through centrifugal spilling out; the giant red stars slowly leak material into space. Rapidly rotating stars may fission into doubles or triples. Some apparently are born into loose gravitation-controlled groups like the Pleiades, and others into the spectacular tight globular clusters. Everywhere the stars and their systems are evolving, some growing heavier by meteorite capture, all losing mass through their radiation.

One of the vicissitudes of star life, which we have mentioned as inevitable and very common, is the birth of planets. Some of the planets bring forth self-replicating macromolecules and organisms—which leads us up to the biological phases of cosmic evolution.

5

On the Origin
and Spread of Life

The investigation of the emergence of the living from the inanimate has rapidly attained top interest scientifically, and, I would add, it should awaken top concern theologically. It rivals in public attention atomic mutations by fusion and fission, as well as the discoveries made with radio telescopes and the flying of artificial satellites.

We have long been confident that living things on this earth developed from the lifeless, with or without the assistance of "miracles." That surmise naturally follows from the chemical analyses of animal bodies. There is no special kind of atom in protoplasm. Our chemical elements are the same as those of the crust of the earth. We are made of hydrogen, carbon, nitrogen, oxygen, calcium, phosphorous, silicon,

55

strontium, and many other common elements. We are of the earth earthy. But how did we get so unearthly complex in structure? And why did we start, anyway?

In the early 1920s the Russian biochemist A. I. Oparin began to think about chemical conditions suitable for the origin of life on the earth. Life could not start full-blown today from inorganic molecules, he and others argue. The now-existent bacteria would devour it, and the abundant free oxygen of the atmosphere would burn it into ashes of various kinds—that is, the oxygen would oxidize the tender molecular aggregates that aspire to the self-replication that we term "living." But there was little or no available oxygen at the beginning of the earth's atmosphere, Oparin points out; it was then locked up in the rocks and water—in SiO_2 and H_2O. Unattached oxygen came into the atmosphere later, chiefly as a by-product of photosynthesis. And, of course, in the beginning there were no murderous bacteria around.

In 1928 J. B. S. Haldane wrote an essay on the early days of the earth and surmised that the energy for chemical evolution might have come from the ultraviolet radiation of the sun. In 1936 Oparin wrote his now famous book, *The Origin of Life*, in which he surveyed the problem, presented some biochemical analyses, gave consideration to the role of the colloidal aggregates, and offered some rather inspired speculation. The book, translated into English by S. Morgulis of Nebraska, has become a classic—a starting point for much of the subsequent work in several American laboratories on life's origin.

Stanley Miller of the University of Chicago published in 1953 his exciting paper on the experiment in which he sent an electric discharge through a mixture of gases and thereby synthesized amino acids, the building blocks of proteins, which are the basic constituents of living matter. The gases in the experiment were those believed to have been the constituents of the primeval atmosphere of the earth—methane, ammonia, water vapor, and hydrogen gas. The electric discharge in the laboratory served as the primitive lightning. Other energy sources, such as gamma rays from natural radioactivity, and the far ultraviolet solar radiation, probably would have done as well.

Miller's synthesis, while not wholly unexpected by the chemically wise, was rather sensational. The experiment was successfully checked in other laboratories, especially by Philip Abelson in Washington. He extended the experiment to other atmospheric compositions, using carbon dioxide and carbon monoxide instead of methane. (The early volcanoes generously provided these gases.) Nitrogen was substituted for ammonia. The results: all the amino acids appeared, some 20 of them, and also some simple proteins. In the laboratory a major step had been taken from the inanimate toward the animate. The experiment has been followed by brilliant researches on nucleic acids, viruses, protein structure, and photosynthesis.

The natural emergence of living organisms in the early history of the earth now seems to have been not only possible but inevitable. Neither miracles nor supernatural operations are needed. It is a great story, but much remains to be done in the laboratory if we are to go continuously from the amino and nucleic acids to the complex self-replicating macromolecules, and much more work if we are to fill in all the steps from the simple carbon compounds to the cytoplasm and other constituents of the living cell.

At this point I shall venture a prediction. In a few years

bright high-school students, either at home or in school laboratories, will synthesize and identify the simpler amino acids. The techniques of biochemistry are very sophisticated, but some clear trails will be laid out by the professional chemists, and moreover, our brightest students are themselves sophisticated. Long before the year 2,000 A.D. the science students will, I predict, do much of the work that the experts now do, and the experts will have cleaned up many of the problems associated with the origin of organisms and perhaps will have successfully tackled the mechanics of the thinking process.

No longer, therefore, need we leave the question of unearthly life to the science-fiction writers. Scientific discoveries and deep cosmic probes have now made it possible to do some tighter thinking on this subject of extraterrestrial life. But first we must remember that life can be variously defined, and clarity for the term is advisable before we report on the relevancies and speculate about the answers.

In adopting a narrow definition, we shall forget about non-biologic "life"—the liveliness of the atoms we breathe, the fast and brief life of electronic states, the vigor of the creeping glaciers, and the energetic rotations of stars and galaxies. All of these in a sense involve the concept of "living." In a broad sense all things and sub-things that take part in animate and inanimate evolution are alive, for they originate, grow, decay, and become dormant or die. We can narrow the field of discussion by writing of self-replicating macromolecules as alive. But in this discussion we are mostly concerned with something "higher" than the primeval self-replicating molecules. Organisms such as those we would recognize as living (or recently alive) on the earth's surface will by definition be the examples of life that concern us here.

As to the spread of life, two preliminary remarks are necessary. First, we cannot yet positively deny, on the basis of direct observation or of biochemical theory in its present stage of development, that life could be based on chemical elements other than those predominant in terrestrial organisms. Life might also exist in physico-chemical and climatological conditions quite unlike those on earth.

Second, conditions and chemistry of air, water, or soils that would poison all of our terrestrial plants and animals might be endured on Mars or elsewhere by organisms that originated and developed under Martian conditions. For example, lichens from our arctic shores might perish promptly if transferred to the colder Martian rocks; nevertheless, Martian-bred lichens probably do exist, and they in turn might wither in our relatively warm arctics and burn up in our oxygen-rich atmosphere.

By "habitable planets" we could choose to mean either planets populated with primates like us or planets capable only of producing and maintaining "low" life and, when conditions are right, the higher sub-human organisms.

HOMO AND THE NARROW SQUEAK

As to the human organism existing elsewhere, I take a dim view. Exact duplication of *Homo sapiens* on another planet is a very long shot, even in this chance-rich universe of stars, space, time, and energy. There are more than a million known variations on the animal theme. Innumerable species of plants and animals have long thrived but eventually failed to survive environmental hazards. At best, they are now fossils in the rocks, and at worst they are undifferentiated constituents of the dust, water, and gas near the earth's surface. It was probably after many a narrow squeak that we of the *Homo sapiens* species got adjusted to successive environmental changes. Many of our fellow anthropoids did not.

As to other planets supporting protoplasmic reactions of some kind, I would put it that living organisms are, and in fact must be, widely distributed throughout the known universe. Their occurrence is a natural, even an inevitable product of molecular evolution. But where are they?

All stars are in motion with respect to one another. Their distances are so great, however, that the actual cross motions on the surface of the sky are extremely small; much precise labor is required to detect and measure them. Only for a relatively few of the nearer stars is precision attained. A double star in Cygnus, with the catalogue number 61 in that constellation, is near enough for its transverse motion to be recorded as sinusoidal. Some unseen celestial neighbor must be causing that wavelike deviation of 61 Cygni from straight-line motion. Similarly wavy paths of stars like Sirius and Procyon are explained by the presence of a companion star, now faintly seen. In each case, the bright star and its faint companion are going around a common center of gravity, just as the earth and moon are revolving in a period of one month around a common center of mass, which lies 1,000 miles below the earth's surface. Actually, 61 Cygni's unseen companion, whose presence is gravitationally demonstrated, is the only definitely recognized planet outside the solar system. From the amount of its gravitational effect on the double star, we believe the companion to be considerably larger than any of our planets. In fact, it may be either a very small dwarf star or a superplanet. Some day we may detect and measure its faint long-wave radiation—"discover" it with a radio telescope which can handle the type of radiation that a superplanet might emit.

With only 61 Cygni's planet detected (and not too widely accepted at that), our consideration of life-bearing planets among the stars must be based not on observation but on circumstantial evidence. This evidence seems to be powerful. I shall merely sketch some of the developments of the past two or three decades that have given strength to our belief in the existence of extraterrestrial life.

Let us take as the habitable zone the region around a star where water, the effective solvent, can exist in its natural liquid state. In our solar system this zone includes the planets Earth, Venus, and Mars. They are within the right interval of distance from the sun. Some of the asteroids also move in this belt, but they can well be ignored, because their small masses hold no atmospheres. Mars is near the outer limit of the belt, Venus rather near the inner limit. If our sun were brighter, the belt would lie further out; if fainter, the belt would be nearer the sun.

To begin, let's consider the Earth only. From the early times of its separate existence it naturally has had an atmosphere. The present character of its surface rocks and other factors have led scientists in several fields to believe that the primitive atmosphere was essentially without free oxygen. It was a reducing atmosphere, dominated by hydrogen. In fact, it is consistent with our knowledge of present planetary atmospheres to hold that the elements hydrogen, carbon, nitrogen, and oxygen (the chief constituents of protoplasm) were present and dominant in the primitive terrestrial atmosphere. These four elements would appear in the form of methane, ammonia, water vapor, and hydrogen gas. With such an atmosphere, in turbulent motion of course, electrical action would be inevitable. Therefore, the energy of lightning and the proper chemical constituents would have been available in the atmosphere billions of years ago for nature's synthesis of the amino acids. And since the available times are so long that even improbable events become inevitable, the building of proteins out of amino acids would also be a natural operation.

The steps in the building up, from the simpler proteins, of macromolecules capable of self-replication can readily be visualized. This bridging, by natural operation, of the gap between the lifeless and the living has in the past decade been taken up so vigorously by the microbiologists and biochemists, with the assistance of the virologists, and has been pursued so successfully, that the production of "test-tube life" is no longer considered impossible.

These new discoveries, which indicate that life can begin, struggle with the environments, and in some cases persist if the chemistry, physics, astronomy, and climates are right, have changed the picture of habitability. Life must exist in nearly all star systems that have planets.

Since life can be a natural evolutionary product on certain planets, the next question therefore concerns the frequency of such suitable planets. If we had strong arguments against the birth and continuity of planets, we might take comfort in the inference that we are unique in the universe —that life is found only on this planet. (Just why that inference would be comforting I do not know.) But the evidence is quite the contrary. There is no likelihood that other planets are nonexistent or even scarce.

ON THE ABUNDANCE OF PLANETS

Many stars are double or triple, perhaps more than half of them. Clusters of stars are common—the open variety like the Pleiades, and the rich globular clusters that have tens of thousands of members. In general, the doubles are hostile to planets like the Earth. They permit no close-in travel in circular or nearly circular paths around them. In fact, double stars would probably not permit the forming of planets from pre-planet material. The same holds for other close groups, like the multiple stars, and probably for the stars in the center of globular star clusters and also the dense nuclear regions of spiral galaxies like our own. But from sampling the contents of space with the largest telescopes to distances in excess of a billion light years, we estimate that there are more than a hundred billion galaxies and a total population of stars in excess of 10^{20}, in excess, that is, of a hundred thousand million billion. If only one star in ten were single like our sun, there would still be a tremendous number of single stars, namely, more than 10^{19}.

In a speculative frame of mind let us say that only one star in a hundred is a single star, and of them only one in a hundred has a system of planets, and of them only one in a hundred has an Earth-like planet, and only one in a hundred Earth-like planets is in that interval of distance from the star that we call the liquid-water belt (neither too cold nor too hot), and of them only one in a hundred has a chemistry of air, water, and land something like ours—suppose all those five chances were approximately true; then only one star in ten billion would have a planet suitable for biological experimentation. But there are so many stars! We would still have, after all that elimination, ten billion planets suitable for organic life something like that on Earth.

In the opinion of most scientists who have pondered this situation in recent years, I have here greatly underestimated the frequency of good planetary sites for biology; I should increase the number by a million times at least—to ten million billion.

Our next problem concerns the probability that life really does exist on some of these accomodating planets. We have life here on Earth, but are we unique? Are all the billions of other suitable planets barren of the products of natural biochemical evolution?

We on Earth have no obvious advantages that are denied to others. In fact, we are very humbly placed in the stellar world. Our planet is small. It circles a very average, yellowish, middle-age star. That star (the sun) is located in the thinly populated outer structure of a large galaxy that contains some 100 billions of other stars, of which many billions must be essentially identical with the sun. That our planet is the one and only place where life has emerged would be a ridiculous assumption. Those who know about the vast number of stars, about the natural ways planets can be born, and the apparently automatic way life emerges when conditions are right—they no longer hesitate to believe that life is a cosmos-wide phenomenon.

Even if only one in a hundred of the ten billion suitable planets has actually got life well under way, there would be more than 100 million such planets. No, it is presumptuous to think that we are alone.

The discovery that the universe is expanding, established by the evidence of the present scattering of the billion-starred galaxies, carries with it the indication that some thousands of millions of years ago (perhaps 10^{10} years) the 100 billion galaxies, and probably all other matter of the recognized universe, were closely compressed into a small volume, perhaps into the speculative primeval supergiant atom of Lemaître. At such time of dense population, disruptive processes, such as collisions, could produce the materials of stars and planets.

Now this time span, several thousand million years, also seems to be the age of the oldest rocks on the Earth's surface. The important conclusion is that the Earth was born in those turbulent, crowded times at or near the beginning of galaxy scattering. Naturally other planetary systems would also date from then. Our sampling tells us that there are literally trillions of stars just like our sun—like it in color, mass, size, temperature, mean density, and other essential properties. Thousands of such stars are in our immediate neighborhood, out here near the edge of our spiral galaxy. Like our sun, some of them must have had the experiences that produce planets.

When we add to these considerations the calculations that the sum total of stars is not less than 10^{20}, and that stars are all radiating the energy necessary for the synthesis of the animate out of the inanimate on whatever planets may be suitably placed, we reach the conclusion that habitable planets are abundant. Great numbers must not only be habitable but must also have experienced the natural evolutionary processes that lead to simple living organisms, which, in turn, over the millennia, lead to the more complicated plants and to the more active, sentient animals.

CONDITIONS NECESSARY FOR PLANETARY LIFE

We can list the most important conditions necessary for the persistence of protoplasmic life, once it is started on a planet, as follows:

1. The star on which it is dependent for warmth and light must be reasonably stable.

2. The planet's orbit must be at least approximately circular.

3. Liquid water must be available, or (most unlikely) some other solvent.

4. The air, oceans, and soils must have a suitable chemical composition (non-poisonous).

5. All organisms must be so conditioned by ignorance or morality that they will not destroy all life, including their own, by poisons or by planet disruption.

This last condition is now the most important for the persistence of life on our own planet.

A few comments are offered on these requirements for continued habitability. The star must not be too irregular in its output of radiation, because it would freeze out planetary life, or incinerate it. The supernova operation, a stellar explosion, would be lethal to neighboring protoplasm.

If life were now, through natural mishap or human madness, completely cleared off the earth, it might not start in this location again. Our present oxygen-rich atmosphere, which was enriched through photosynthesis as soon as chlorophyll plants appeared, would probably oxidize any macromolecules that aspired to self-replication.

A considerable diversity in the abundances of the various chemical elements could be tolerated *if* the planetary life grew up under those diverse conditions. Also, much diversity could be allowed in the temperatures, in the shape of the planet's orbit, and in the rotation and revolution periods, if the proper vital adjustments were made to meet the prevailing conditions. We organisms have in the past billion years survived easily much mountain building, wide desiccations, flooding, and advancing ice sheets.

LIFE IN THE SOLAR SYSTEM

We learn from the spectrum analysis of stars and nebulae that there is a common chemistry the world over—the same chemical elements everywhere. It is now believed by experts in the subject that there must be also a universal biochemistry. Keeping in mind the listed "conditions necessary for planetary life," let us examine possible solar-system sites for the emergence and persistence of that delicate biological operation.

Could there be living organisms on the surface of the sun? Or inside? Of course not, for the surface temperature is about 10,000° F., sun-spot temperatures about 6,000° F., and internal temperatures in the millions of degrees. These temperatures would make viable macromolecules impossible. The simple molecule H_2O could not exist, and for the origin and evolution of organisms such as we recognise on the Earth we must have water in a liquid state. Therefore, no protoplasmic life on the sun, and for the same reason no life on any of the radiant stars.

MERCURY, the nearest of all planets to the sun, is in a peculiar situation. One side is forever facing the nearby sun, the other side facing away. There can be no liquid water on the planet, since on the sunny side the temperature is nearly 800° F., and on the black back side it must be very far below zero. In the latter place it is too cold for water and life of any kind; in the other, too hot. How about the twilight zone between the sizzling hot and congealing cold? Any life there? No, for several reasons, the chief being that the mass of Mercury is only a twentieth that of the earth and all gases in the atmosphere would escape into space. There would be and could be no permanent atmosphere. All life, by our definition, requires air and water. Mercury is, therefore, certain to be a lifeless desert.

(In passing it is of interest to record that probably much fewer than half of the professional astronomers of modern times have ever seen the planet Mercury. It always stays in the sky near the sun and is difficult to pick up visually near sunrise and sunset. And anyway, many astronomers do not "fool around" with small affairs. In ancient times observers —around the Mediterranean—did see Mercury easily and often, for then there was much less trouble with street lights and smog.)

VENUS, the second planet, is seen by everybody. Much of the time it is the brightest planet in the sky, and thus is generally miscalled the "Evening Star" or the "Morning Star." Until recently the question of life or no life on Venus could not be decided. Clouds of nitrogen and carbon dioxide, possibly also of dust, completely blanket the surface, and no markings can be seen. Under these circumstances this "twin" of the earth was left to the imaginations of the fiction writers, at least as far as the length of the Venus day and the nature of the surface are concerned. By some writers vital "Venusians" were imagined—strange, beclouded creatures that never saw sunlight. At times in the past, weak evidence was put forward in favor of a short rotation period, but other evidence was advanced in favor of a long day, perhaps 225 earth days, the same as the period of revolution of Venus around the sun.

Now the puzzles are at least partly solved, and the Venusians have become historical only. The conclusion that there can be no protoplasmic life on Venus came as the result of advances in electronics and space flight. The radio telescope, the development of which was a by-product of World War II, first settled the matter by penetrating the cloud blanket and finding that Venus emits long-wave radiation characteristic of surfaces with temperatures above 600° F. Then in 1962 our spacecraft messenger, Mariner II, measured the surface temperature to be 800° F. That disposes of the life question.

The radio telescopes not only answer the temperature and life questions but also indicate, according to the most widely accepted observations, that the rotation period (the Venus day) is the same as the orbital period—that is, 225 of our days. If so, Venus always keeps the same face to the sun, as does Mercury. But because of its moving gaseous atmosphere, the temperatures on the day and night sides do not conspicuously differ as they do on Mercury.

By bouncing radar waves off the planet's surface, we now have a means of measuring accurately the mean distance to Venus, and from that result we shall eventually obtain improved measures throughout the whole solar system, since the masses, velocities, and distances are all interrelated.

The EARTH requires here no special consideration. Everyone admits the existence of life on Planet No. 3, and it appears in millions of different forms—plant and animal. There are more than 200,000 kinds of beetles, 3,500 species of ants, and much of the Earth's surface is not yet thoroughly explored. Of *Homo* there is but one species—*sapiens*, so-called.

One further remark on the Earth's biology. Life has existed on its surface for at least one and a half billion years, according to the best tests of the ages of the fossils in the oldest sedimentary rocks. Therefore the strength of the sunlight necessary for photosynthesis has been essentially constant for all those years. From that conclusion we are led to another: namely, that to keep the sun steady in radiation for such a long time, an unfailing source of solar energy must be found. Gravitational compression would not suffice for so long, or meteor infall, or just simple burning of whatever molecular material is available. The source was sought and found to be the burning of hydrogen as fuel into helium as ash in the center of the sun—that is, transforming hydrogen atoms into helium atoms and shortwave gamma radiation. The temperature required for this operation is about twelve million degrees. By the time this heat has "leaked" to the surface of the sun, it has come down to the comfortable thermostated temperature of about 10,000° F. that flows into cold space. Of the sun's total radiation, one two-billionth part falls on the Earth, thus providing our steady light and heat.

We have here a good illustration of the profitable tie-ups between sciences (paleobotany joining astrophysics): the age of fossil algae on the Earth bears on the mutations of chemical elements in the center of a star 93 million miles away.

MARS is the most talked about member of the sun's family, except for our obsession with the Earth. The Martian appeal is as much romantic as scientific. Hundreds of hypothetical space travelers and exaggerators have brought Mars and the off-human Martians into their fictions. From a purely astronomical standpoint there is much of interest—so much, in fact, that our modern astronauts have listed Mars for a visit as soon as the lunar curiosity is satisfied.

The easily observed seasonal changes on the Martian surface are responsible for much of our interest, for the best interpretation of these changes holds that they are biological. But the biology on that No. 4 planet must be tough, judged by terrestrial standards. The air is thin, the temperature cold (minus 40° F. on the average), with oxygen very scarce, and just enough water and water vapor to produce in the Martian winter some polar ice caps (or possibly caps of hoar frost). In the summer seasons, however, there is a little water, and therefore simple forms of life are not impossible.

When the astronauts arrive and land on Mars, they must have along their customary earthly environment, the same as for landings on the moon. Probably all kinds of living things such as we have on the Earth would promptly die if transferred to Mars. But that does not mean that life could not have originated independently on Mars and become adjusted to the physical conditions there prevailing. We humans could not adjust to the harsh Martian conditions, but possibly our Earth's low algal forms might survive temporarily.

Why is the Martian air so thin? Clearly because the planet's mass and surface gravity are small compared with the Earth's. The Martian air is probably nitrogen for the most part, with a good deal of carbon dioxide; the original supply of oxygen, if any, has been depleted in the rusting of the surface rocks, which has given the planet its reddish color. Some have ascribed the localized changes in color in part or wholly to seasonal dust storms, or even to lava flows, but vegetation remains as the best interpretation, and therefore the one-word reply to the question: "Life on Mars?" is "Probably."

ASTEROIDS by the tens of thousands, moving in orbits mostly between those of Mars and Jupiter, are airless, waterless, and therefore lifeless. They have not enough mass to hold either air or water. If they did originate, as many believe, from the bursting of one or more planets, we may rightly surmise that the organic compounds recently discovered in analyses of meteorites point to the former existence of a planetary site for life, a site that once existed on the outer fringe of the sun's liquid-water belt. But at present that suggestion is crass speculation.

JUPITER is now getting some attention from the "life-site" hunters. In the past it was ruled out as too cold, because of its great distance from the sun, but recent studies of the "greenhouse effect" on the Earth and elsewhere suggest that Jupiter might qualify for habitation. The surprisingly high temperature of Venus is properly ascribed to its thick atmosphere acting like the glass of a greenhouse, transmitting inward the sunlight but cutting down the outward Venus radiation. If the greenhouse effect also prevails on Jupiter, its surface may be warmed up from its temperature of minus 200° F. to something livable.

SATURN, the second largest in the sun's family, is disqualified as a site for organic existence because its temperature is more than 240° below zero Fahrenheit—much too cold for protoplasm, even with some help from greenhousing. The atmosphere is hydrogen gas, adulterated with methane (marsh gas) and ammonia snow, and it is so thick that the planet as a whole is a lightweight; it would float on water. The picturesque rings of Saturn are collections of moonlets —billions of them. They are probably composed of ice-covered pebbles, and of course are lifeless, as also must be the planet's nine satellites. The satellite Titan, which is much larger than the Earth's moon, has an atmosphere of methane, according to G. P. Kuiper, a high authority on planetary atmospheres. But there can be no Titan biology—it is much too cold.

URANUS and NEPTUNE are hopelessly frigid, and so are their satellites. Both are far from the sun; PLUTO, the ninth and remotest of the sun's major planets, is colder still—perhaps minus 350° F. Farther out are some long-period comets and countless meteors, but our survey by now has passed far beyond the realm where the sun can provide life-sustaining radiation in sufficient strength.

Life elsewhere among the stars? In the Harvard spectrum catalogues, compiled by Annie Cannon, are at least 40,000 nearby stars very much like the sun in size, color, temperature, motion, affiliations, and candlepower. In our galaxy as a whole there must be billions of replicas of our sun, and likewise in the billions of other galaxies. Probably about half of these sunlike stars have planets, and certainly many millions will have planets like the Earth in many qualities, such as distance from their stars, size, chemical make-up, daylength, and age.

Since we have learned the mechanism of the emergence of the animate from the inanimate, the living from the not and never alive, and have proposed that we ourselves are but one item in the stream of evolution from atoms to macromolecules to organisms to man and other higher animals, we are in a proper position to say confidently that there must be life—living biochemicals—all over the universe.

In some of the innumerable places where life occurs, the

biological evolution may indeed be very similar to what we know here on Earth. But we must remember that there are millions of variations on the plant and animal themes. Hence a belief in the exact duplication anywhere of *Homo sapiens* is not very sapient!

6

The Human Response to an Expanding Universe

We started with the birth and growth of atoms and speedily progressed through a myriad of atomic, molecular, stellar and cellular stages to universal life. Where does mankind fit into all this? What sort of perspective does this knowledge give him regarding his own future?

In the middle of the twentieth century we have burst into a new realm of knowledge which is bound to impel fundamental alterations in our view of the destiny of our species— and its possibilities. In the microcosmos, the physicist is dismembering the atom and measuring the quantum, and the biologist is unraveling the mysteries of the gene. In the macrocosmos, the astronomer is exploring an expanding universe of billions of galaxies, each with its billions of stars, and the mathematician has regularized beautiful concepts concerning the interiors of stars and the history of space-time. The new astronomical and biochemical revelations establish firmly our belief in the cosmos-wide occurrence of life. When we add the discovery that the sun, planets, and naked-eye stars are indifferently located at the edge of one ordinary galaxy, we establish man's place in the universe as less unique than his vanity pictured it a brief century ago.

Before we venture some remarks on what might be the human response to an expanding world of galaxies, and to an explosively expanding knowledge of atoms, genes, stars, and natural laws, a foundation can be laid, first by examining the possibility of man's long survival on the earth, and secondly by surveying the intellectual equipment that is available for his understanding of cosmic behavior and for responding to it constructively.

FISH OR *HOMO*—THAT IS THE QUESTION

The protoplasmic experiment, as we may designate life, is an illuminating demonstration of Nature's intricacies. We are probably much more complex in body and mind, much more wonderfully made, than we know. The human imagination, versatile as it is, would be hard put to dream up such complexities and co-ordinations as those achieved inside the living cell, and the imagination would be equally far surpassed by full knowledge of the real mechanism at the center of a large molecule. Fiction appears to lag far behind the facts. The yet Undiscovered, the still Unknown, so far "transcends the what we know" that a very rich and happy future of inquiry and discovery lies ahead.

To me it is a sign that we are sincere subscribers to the "growth" motif that threads and spreads through the universe, to the growth certainly of man's mind if not of his body, to the evolution of races if not of individuals, when we inquire what lies ahead for mankind—what lies far, far ahead in the times when the galaxies will have scattered, the moon receded to its coming faintness, and the massive mountains will have been worn away by the persistently weathering winds and rains. What then of the sun and the Earth? What then of terrestrial biology? What then have we grown into?

Since men in the future must continue to rely for survival on their natural wits and acquired wisdom, and since they are embattled in a continual contest with a Nature that includes their dangerous selves, we are led to worry and wonder whether proud man or the meek will eventually inherit the earth. As an example of the meek I might choose the fish. They employ chiefly instincts, not heavy forebrains.

Fish or *Homo*—that is the question. Which animal type will be here 10,000 years from now; which will more likely fall the victim of fate or folly? The answer, of course, is too obvious, painfully obvious. The fish have been here several hundred million years; man, but a few hundred thousand. The oceans are stable enough in their salinity, temperature, and food supplies to suit indefinitely a thousand species of fish. It is difficult to imagine a way of curtailing the life of that class of animals without complete disruption of the planet, or the poisoning of the plankton food in all the seven seas. But 10,000 years is a pretty long time for Homo. His structure and social manners do not make him a good insurance risk. How will he eventually be dispossessed?

WHAT OPPOSES MAN'S SURVIVAL?

About three-fourths of the earth's crust is under the oceans; the remainder protrudes above the water level to various heights. There is some advance and recession of the shore lines. The mountains rise up through the wrinkling of the earth's crust, and are worn down by the winds and rains. In general, however, the continents seem to be pretty stable over geological eras. Extrapolating into the future, we should say that it is extremely unlikely that man will be drowned out of existence by the rising sea or desiccated by lack of water. A man-eliminating deluge is not in the cards, nor is a worldwide, totally lethal drought.

Let us take a wider view and consider sketchily the project of a complete extermination of the human race. In what manner might we, as agents of Nature (or the devil), devise the elimination of *Homo sapiens?* First we set a time limit for the operation—not too short, not too long. Let us examine the probability of man not being on the earth's surface 10,000 years from now.

We begin with macrocosmic instruments for eradication. What is the possibility or probability of a collision of the earth with a star? If the earth or even the sun were struck by one of those stellar masses, our goal would be achieved: terrestrial biology would be finished. But the stars are so widely separated that collisions are out of the question in our chosen short time interval of 10,000 years. The probabilities are overwhelmingly against trouble with stars.

Appreciating that escape, let us then ask about the sun cooling down enough to freeze us out, or blowing up into a nova and incinerating the planet. No likelihood at all, or at least highly improbable, for the sun appears to be a relatively stable type of star; its radiation has been steady for many hundreds of millions of years. Its hydrogen content is ample to supply energy, produced by atomic fusion, for a million times 10,000 years.

Safe from annihilation by stars and sun, should we fear some misbehavior of the earth, such as its abandoning orbital regularity and getting too near the sun or too far away? The answer is No. Our observations and mathematical analyses show that the planetary orbits are completely stable over time intervals such as we are here considering. The earth moves in what is practically a vacuum, in a nearly circular path around the sun, and neither its daily rotation nor its yearly revolution will change perceptibly in the allotted hundred centuries. (We can of course adapt ourselves to the coming and going of the ice sheets, such as those that occurred in the northern hemisphere during the past hundred thousand years.)

Already we have mentioned the relative constancy in the height of continents and depths of oceans. Terrestrial life has readily adjusted itself to the ups and downs of land and sea in the past million years, and in the next 10,000 years the slow-moving mountains and shore lines will present little danger.

Poison the atmosphere with an over-abundance of volcanic gases and make it unbreathable by land animals, including man? Well, such has not happened in the past 500 million years and it is certainly unlikely in the next 10,000; the earth is gradually getting over its eruptive birth-pangs.

Outer space presents some dangers—noxious gases, meteors, and cosmic rays. But the poisoning of our atmosphere by interstellar gas and dust is a very long chance. The gas in space is mostly non-poisonous hydrogen and helium, and its distribution is so thin that our own nitrogen-oxygen atmosphere shields us completely. It protects us also from the tiny, high-speed interplanetary meteors and from lethal radiations.

To summarize the progress so far in this project of eliminating man (and other animals) from the earth's surface, we get no likely help from the stars, from interstellar dust, from the sun's radiation or its lack, from the deviation of the earth from its present orbit, from deadly climates, or from the chemistry of the earth's land, air, and water.

We turn to the biological sciences. The large beasts are no longer a threat, nor, in fact, are any of the plant and animal forms. We are now competent also to cope with bacteria, viruses, and the like, at least sufficiently well to keep our species going, even if millions perished in some wild epidemic.

Of course some worldwide disaster *could* happen, coming to us anywhere from star crash to infective protein, but the chances are heavily against it—less than one chance in a million, I would surmise, for trouble with astronomical bodies, less than one in a thousand for serious difficulties with climate, volcanoes, worldwide floods, or desiccation, and perhaps less than one chance in a hundred for planet-wide incurable diseases.

(Even if 99 per cent of the world's population of *Homo sapiens* should fall foul of sudden disaster, there would yet be left more than 25 million humans rapidly reseeding the earth; therefore the total-elimination effort would have been a failure. Spoiling a culture or civilization is one thing, and perhaps not too arduous; complete eradication of a widespread organic species is quite another, and vastly more difficult.)

In other words, man seems to have a healthy prospect, a long security from stars, climate, and terminating germs. But wait! I have not named the real danger, and it is bleakly ominous, as everyone in these days agrees. The danger is man himself. He is his own worst enemy. He is acquiring tools and studying techniques which might solve the problem of attaining complete elimination of *Homo* from the planet Earth.

What mental and moral equipment do we possess, we may now ask, that would justify, for our species of *Homo*, the name *sapiens*, and that might justify hopes for mankind's survival?

MAN'S MAJOR HALLUCINATIONS

We who read, write, and contemplate have minds that have been laboriously taught. The teaching has been done by books and teachers, and by our own efforts. Through such instruction we have attained a rather high degree of competence. We can get around physically with reasonable safety, and react to our environment intelligently and with pardonable pride. But without the instruction that started a few hours after birth, we would not be doing very well. We have needed help from the very beginning—in decreasing amount, to be sure, but nevertheless we have been dependents all our lives. Instincts, such as we attribute to the newly hatched, uncared-for mosquito or housefly, are not sufficient at our birth to keep us alive for a week. When neglected, we can only howl instinctively for nourishment. A very primitive performance. Later a more subtle "howling" for food is taught us, and continues in use. That subtlety is a part and product of our training.

The housefly, on the other hand, is born with her training completed. For the planning and executing of life's operations, for making emergency decisions and acting thereon, she uses not only her individual nervous ganglia but also, and mainly, her *generic* mind—equipment that we largely lack. For man, the ratio of the number of voluntary decisions to the number that the experience of the race has built into us is high, because so little is built in. The housefly makes some decisions of her own, but mostly she uses the gradually acquired, slowly trained mind of thousands of generations of flies. Insect and man—one automatic to a high degree, the other self-conscious—they are alike in responding to "nerve" stimulation but different in the degree or intensity of their "brain" reactions.

In view of the width of the cosmos and the slim hold on existence that Nature has provided for *Homo sapiens*, it would seem properly modest if we talked less about man being superior, less about his being the anointed of the gods. Who was anointed, and by whom, we ask, throughout the half-billion manless Paleozoic and Mesozoic years when thousands of kinds of wonderful animals sought and fought for survival on the earth? Who was then the Anointed?

Some claimants for human distinction say that man's superiority arises from his "historical sense." They have in mind, probably, the histories written by such as Gibbon, Parkman, and Toynbee. Or, thinking a little deeper, they also have in mind the word-of-mouth transmission of the unwritten folklore of the past few thousand years. And there is unwritten history, still more basic, in the mother's murmuring of do's and don't's to her dimly responding infant; she is setting up his "historical sense." But how does this differ, except in degree, from the sparrow chirping to her young, or the worker ants twiddling antennae with the newly emerged callows? And has not the impelling sex urge of a million kinds of animals in a sense recited the deep and moving history of the ages—recited it more profoundly, more insistently than we vain primates have done by scratching symbols on cavern walls or by binding our more systematic scratchings into octavo volumes?

"But only man," you may argue, "acts on the basis of historical knowledge." Again, nonsense. In the first place, he does not act very well: he goes right on fighting thoughtless, futile wars, goes on behaving in a fashion more beastly than angelic. History appears to teach him little. And secondly, in their own manner most animals also act on the basis of experience. The survival of the so-called fittest is the result of an organism's adjustment to facts.

There can be no better laboratory for the elaboration of thoughts on man's orientation in a complex world than a flowering meadow, or a noisy brook, or a spiral galaxy. For the green leaves of the meadow are sucklings of a star's radiation. The rapids in a brook, responding to universal gravitation, perform erosions such as those that have worn down to oblivion the lofty pre-Alps and the primitive Appalachians. The hundred-ton maple tree that calmly dreams through the decades is in the same universe as the Andromeda galaxy with its billions of seething stars. The tree heeds the impulse of gravity according to the same rules as those subscribed to by the stars in a globular cluster. Further, the tree is made of the same complex molecular aggregates as are the birds in its branches, the parasites on its roots, and the philosophers who wonder about it.

In our complex universe one simple requirement stands out: we must link ourselves with all the other phenomena that participate in life. We must go beyond life and associate ourselves continually and insistently with the solid rocks of the earth, the gaseous winds of the sky. Of course, it is our privilege to fancy ourselves as the thinkers and prognosticators for all earthly organisms of the past, present, and future, for all the stars and nebulae, for all the basic entities. We may cherish the hallucination that we are dominant because we can think and can make a pattern for all the world.

A close student of social insects, however, will not boast about the superiority of man's social awareness, and he may even qualify the claim for superiority of the human brain. He has seen too much of the wonderful—this student of animal societies. He has seen the honeybee dance her complex geometry, instructing by sight and scent and diagram her student gatherers of honey and pollen. He has witnessed the magic of many insects carrying out their complicated enterprises.

"But we alone can reason," you insist. But that is a totally unreasonable assumption. What evidence is there of thoughtlessness and unreason in the bird choosing its nesting site or a spider locating its web? The generic mind has a great deal to do with controlling the decisions, but the behavior shows an appropriate adjustment to the immediate situation. In contrast, we primates are short on inheritance but long on ability to cope with the environmental unusual. A matter of degree or intensity is here again indicated—not a different kind of thinking and reasoning. In some characteristics and skills we do not excel; we only approach the abilities of other animals, and sometimes not very closely. In other characteristics and skills, such as reading symbols, they approach us, though not too closely. In differing degrees the higher mammals have all of our virtues and vices, our abilities and futilities.

The teaching of all this is: Don't take man too seriously, even when orienting him among the plants and animals on this local planet, and certainly not when comparing him with possibilities elsewhere in the richly endowed Metagalaxy.

But let us not tire ourselves with annoyance at man's egocentric vanities. Rather than abuse the presumptuous primate, we should simply call attention to the existence of the generic mind, the most precious inheritance of most animal forms. We point also to the success, over the millions of years, of thousands of animal species that have acquired security by methods lost to us, lost to us animals who must resort, for survival, to mother murmurings, folk tales, and printed history.

OUR LIMITED SENSE ORGANS

When we turn from the mind to the senses through which we perceive nature, our self-esteem again is healthily eroded.

Seeing and hearing provide our best methods of ascertaining what is what, and why. The eyes and the ears—without them it would be a strange world. With better eyes and ears, and with additional sense organs, we might have attained long ago a much finer cosmic knowledge than we have up to now.

The major part of our knowledge of the universe has in the past come through information provided by one sense organ alone—that of vision. Our eyes, however, are sensitive only in a small section of the wide radiation spectrum. They respond to stimulations only from the violet to the red—over much less than two octaves. Through the development of sensory artifices, however, we have learned to explore nature with radiations extending over a range of more than 50 octaves: from cosmic rays through gamma rays, X-rays, the ultraviolet, the visible blue-to-red radiation that our eyes record, the infrared (heat waves), radio, and on to electric power wavelengths that are measured in miles. We know and measure and use these off-color radiations not directly with the retinas of our eyes, as we do with light, but with the retinas, we might say, of photographic plates, Geiger counters, photocells, masers, lasers, and transistors.

We are doing pretty well with the equipment Nature provided. But the eyes and other sense organs arose naturally to serve animals in the practical problems of existence, not for use in profound thought and for researches into the nature and operations of the universe. Practical existence did not until recently require "impractical" knowledge. But now our intellectual desires have gone ahead of our built-in sensory receptors. Even when we supplement the sense of vision with our sense of hearing, with our poor sense of smell, and a complex of tactile senses, we are not yet well-equipped intrinsically to cope with cosmic mysteries. In fact, as an organism ambitious to know, and know deeply, man is rather primitive in his senses (his primitivism in body anatomy is, of course, generally recognized).

Every human sense receptor, except possibly that concerned in tone discrimination, is outdone by the corresponding receptor of one terrestrial animal or another—by the hawk's vision, the dog's hearing, the insect's smelling. However, the sensory shortcomings, and the resulting failure to comprehend fully much of nature, may be only a local hominid deficiency. On the basis of the new estimates of the great abundance of stars and the high probability of millions of planets with highly developed life, we are made aware— embarrassingly aware—that we may be intellectual minims in the life of the universe. This uncomfortable idea can be further developed by pointing out that sense receptors, in quality quite unknown to us and in fact hardly imaginable, which record phenomena of which we are totally ignorant, may easily exist among the higher sentient organisms of other planets.

Sometimes we suspect that many animal and plant forms on this planet may possess senses other than those we recognize in ourselves—not merely extended ranges of hearing or of vision or of smell but entirely different responses. The bees and ants respond, as we do not, to polarized light; the birds and fish in migration—to what? And there are those among us who dream of vestigial or embryonic senses hovering about the human psyche.

GROWTH THROUGH UNDERSTANDING

To summarize our cosmic self-appraisal: We are primitive in a sensory sense. We are incurably peripheral, on a remote edge of a billion-starred galaxy. With help from our star we have slowly evolved from the wonder-working Archaeozoic ooze in which so many biological experiments were made. We have arisen from the same primeval Hot Thin Soup* from which also evolved bluebirds and roses and a million other wonderfully constructed organisms. We must henceforth live with awareness of these cosmic facts and of our ancestry, no matter how disturbing such knowledge is to rigid creeds. With much less convincing evidence than now at hand, we have been for a century vaguely aware of our immediate anthropoid ancestry.

---

* The phrase of J. B. S. Haldane.

The cosmic immensities, whether of space and time or of outlook and concept, should not, however, dismay us, the local gropers and interpreters. In our natural program of growth through understanding, each day competes with our yesterdays. Fortunately for us that competition, that striving and groping, is largely inborn, nicely automatic; our succeeding days compete as a matter of course. If care is taken to oppose vigorously the natural regressions that often ensue from static conformity, we shall continue to evolve with the rotating of the planets and the radiating of the suns. We grow naturally with the passage of time, as do the animals and the plants.

We have reached a stage where this automatic, slow, slight, and hesitant rising is no longer enough for us—the considerably intelligent and somewhat informed species self-styled *Homo sapiens*. But we can consciously speed up our development. What we should strive for is not growth in size, or strength, or longevity, but growth primarily in the qualities that we associate with mind, a development that includes those fine indefinables—heart and spirit. And therein lies the nucleus of our cosmic ethic. The evidence clearly shows that we have the potentiality not only of conforming to the cosmic theme of Growth but perhaps even of elaborating or revising some of its natural rules. Indeed, each day can and should compete with all the yesterdays of our species.

Anthropocentric religions and philosophies, which have so often been conspicuously earthbound and much ensnarled in the human mind and human behavior, have in these present days an opportunity for aggrandizement through incorporating a sensibility of the newly revealed cosmos. If the theologian finds it difficult to take seriously our insistence that the god of humanity is equally the god of gravitation and the god of spiral galaxies, at least he may be willing to consider the reasonableness of extending to all the higher sentient beings that have evolved elsewhere among the myriads of galaxies the same intellectual or spiritual rating he gives to us. A one-planet deity has for me little appeal.

The new knowledge from many sources—from the test tube, from the extended radiation spectrum, the electron microscope, experimental agriculture, and the radio telescope, from mathematical equations and the cosmotrons—the revelations from all these, which were wholly unknown to the ancient cosmologists and prophets, make obsolete many of the earlier world views. The new discoveries and developments contribute to the unfolding of a magnificent universe; to be a participant therein is also magnificent. With our confreres on distant planets, with our fellow animals and plants of the Earth's land, sea and air, with the rocks and waters of all planetary crusts, with the photons and atoms that make up the stars—with all these we are associated in an existence and an evolution that inspire respect and deep reverence.

There are those who would call this attitude their philosophy, their religion. Their thoughts would hesitate, I hope, to retreat from the grand galaxies to the parasitic earth; would be unwilling to come out of the cosmic depths and durations to concern themselves only with one organic species on the crust of one small planet, near a commonplace star, at the edge of one of the myriad galaxies. In their search for the Ultimate we trust that they get glimpses of a far-reaching Stellar Theology.

CONFESSING TO OPTIMISM

It seems proper to conclude this discussion of man's response to the expanding universe on a note of humility and hope, if not of high confidence. Certainly we should be humble about our trivial progress toward understanding the total of the external world. We know enough to get along, as do most of the other animals. We can cope with all the physical challenges. And going further, we can construct new worlds of ideas and beauty.

We optimists assume that the human mind and heart will successfully confront the dangers to mankind as they arise. Our habitation on a pretty steady planet is comfortable on the average, and may get happier. We have increased the length of our useful lives. We have built up ethical systems that average to bring us safety and satisfaction, although they worry us deeply by frequent failures. We know that the rules of the stars are hard, that the flow of time is irreversible, that death is dark and will accept no substitutes. But even so, the lights can, if we cooperate, exceed the shadows. The imagination can enter when knowledge falters. We of the higher primates have delved into the cosmic facts deeply enough to recognize the need of cosmic fancies when facts are delayed. But as rational practitioners of life and tentative interpreters of the cosmos, we oppose superstition—the last stronghold of the irrational—and we deny miracles. Thanks to man's reasoning, belief in the supernatural is now tempered with thought. Science has captured many outposts in our necessarily continuous conflict with the Tyranny of the Unknown. We no longer need appeal to anything beyond Nature when we are confronted by such problems as the origin of life, or the binding forces of nucleons, or the orbits in a star cluster, or the electrochemical dynamics of a thought. We can assail all such questions rationally.

It is my own belief that the central motive of biological existence is to grow in refined complexity, in durability, in adaptability. Man, as half beast, half angel, must of course comply with the biogenic common law, but he is able to make amendments thereto. It is probable, and certainly deeply to be desired, that the men of the future will correct our shortcomings and build on the basis of our thoughts and acts a finer mental and social structure—one that is in better keeping with Nature's heavy investment in the locally dominant human race.

7

Stars, Ethics, and Co-existence

We have concluded that we are not alone in the universe—that life is a natural, cosmos-wide phenomenon not confined to our small planet—and further concluded that the only serious threat to mankind's survival is man himself. The distortions of civilization now seem to foreshadow the possibility of extinction of our kind. For the race of men, and for the individual man, there are ominous portents of a final curtain.

Is this man's most likely fate? Or might we not rather look forward to a growth of social wisdom and glorious survival—toward the evolution of a kind of superman rather than toward extinction? All depends on whether we can learn the secret of co-existence.

Co-existence with the stars? Certainly—no problem there. With life elsewhere? Again—no problem, at least for the foreseeable future. Co-existence with our fellow men on this planet? Ah—there is the difficulty.

Before we explore that subject, let us give a moment's consideration to the rather remote prospect of encounters with life on other planets. The evidence is strong that there is some kind of life on Mars, and our space flights may soon resolve that question. If these explorations prove the existence of Martian life, however primitive, our conjectures as to the probability of the existence of more complex forms of life on suitable planets throughout the universe will be greatly strengthened. It is very unlikely that any forms will be found exactly like the higher primates on the earth, but thinking, communicating creatures are highly probable.

Will we be forever out of physical and mental contact with the sentient beings on the distant planets? Some scientists think not. They have recently been discussing possible techniques for communicating, by light and radio signals, across the emptiness of space. A few brief attempts have been made to "listen" with radio telescopes for possible coded signals at a universal wavelength (the "song of hydrogen"). But they have caught nothing intelligible, and there is not much hope for early success.

It is properly assumed, I believe, that organisms more "advanced" than we are exist on planets within reach of our transmitters. But effective two-way communication would be very difficult. Probably the nearest inhabited planet is at least ten light years (60 trillion miles) away. A single question and answer, traveling at the velocity of light, would take more than 20 years.

Perhaps we should first attempt reciprocated communication with non-human organisms here on the earth—say with a vegetable, or a scarab beetle, or a termite queen-mother, who represents the highest natural societal organization known on this planet. Foolish suggestions, yes, but they suggest the difficulty and probable impossibility of interplanetary communication. We are effectively isolated from other life-bearing planets by the physics of the situation.

THE ETHICAL CRISIS

Leaving the rather bizarre problem of contact with life elsewhere for the future, we turn back to the serious problem of co-existence on this planet. Its seriousness has been vastly intensified by man's new-found ability to control the reactions producing nuclear energy (the same reactions that created the elements of the material universe). The atomic age has precipitated mankind into a profound ethical crisis, since nuclear energy has such tremendous potentialities for good or for bad.

The hydrogen atom is capable of doing great things for the human race. It is an inexhaustible source of cosmic fuel —which cannot be said of wood or coal or oil. If we can learn to harness it properly, the hydrogen atom can easily give us essentially free energy everywhere on the planet. The imagination is made giddy by the grandeur of man's future if hydrogen is his ally. But that happy collaboration remains to be created—not by some single act but by a series of deliberate acts aimed to serve all mankind.

Our scientific and technological progress on many fronts makes new ethical attitudes imperative. We need an ethical system suitable for the now—for this age, rather than for the human society of 2,000 years ago. Cautiously but certainly, we must modernize our ethics.

We require a suitable set of principles for the guidance of today's policy-makers, and for today's actors on the international stage. The scientist's atom has made good will, good fellowship, social justice, and decency more than ever essential if degradation, and eventually extinction, are to be avoided. To our problems, especially to our multi-racial and multi-national problems, peaceful approaches are demanded. Angry men cannot resolve our social and political dilemmas. Big national angers can no longer be tolerated if man is to survive. For anger leads to action and reaction and counteraction. If atomic war tools are available to angry and vain and stupid men, and are used—then a grim final curtain will close the human ploy on this planet. It will truly be a judgment day—a day of our own *bad* judgment. The galaxies will continue to rotate, without concern for little Planet No. 3 and its highest life (which is not quite high enough). The sun will bountifully pour its energy into space, but not for *Homo*. He will be through because he has not learned to live with himself.

But let us turn the page and be optimistic; let us consider some elementary, short-term alternatives to the extinction of *Homo sapiens*. Only short-term protections they will be, but long enough, I hope, to give us an opportunity to establish long-term working plans, such as enforcible world law, which could restrain indefinitely the genocidal, suicidal madness of man's worst enemy—man himself.

THE COMMON BREATH OF HUMANITY

To put ourselves in a proper mood for optimistic thoughts, we need a new evaluation. Take a deep breath, please, and hold tight, for I am taking you on a tour of the universe, on a quick trip to the corners of the world, on an exploration of unusual perspectives—all in the interest of a discussion of the one world of mankind. We shall talk of simple things, starting with that deep breath, which you may now distribute into surrounding space.

That breath, which you found so necessary and natural, unites you quietly with the rest of us all over the earth. It was a volume of the moving air of your immediate locality, and most of it has now gone forth to join again the winds of the planet, to join the international stock of terrestrial atmosphere.

A year from now I shall breathe in and out a good many thousands of the nitrogen molecules which a minute ago were in the Deep Breaths of all of you; and wherever you are, on whatever continent, you, too, will be re-breathing some of the Deep Breath of a minute ago. I shall, unknowingly, have intimate association with you, and, of course, you with me. This may sound unhygienic, a little more intimate than you like, but it is true. Let us consider further the simple arithmetic and argument that concern internationalism in breathing.

Some breaths are big, some are small; a deep, full breath weighs a little less than three-fourths of a gram. That is, there are about 600 breaths in a pound of air. Good air is about 78 per cent nitrogen gas and about 21 per cent oxygen. (There are also small amounts of carbon dioxide, argon, and other gases.)

Knowing that the breath weighs something like three-fourths of a gram, I can easily compute the approximate number of nitrogen atoms in that breath. The number is inconceivably large, because atoms are inconceivably small. The number is so large that it is hard to pronounce. One way of expressing the number of nitrogen atoms in a deep breath is to say that it is two point four times ten to the twenty-second power. That is the hard way. Another way is to say 24 thousand million million million. It's an appalling number. There were, in fact, in your Deep Breath more than ten million million times as many nitrogen atoms as there are people living on this planet. There were more than a hundred billion times as many nitrogen atoms as there are stars in our galaxy. You do, indeed, whenever you breathe, take on more numerically than you may have appreciated. And now, where are those 24 thousand million million million nitrogen atoms that you expelled? They are mingling with other nitrogen and oxygen atoms of the atmosphere, and in the course of time they will be so thoroughly mixed by the winds of the land and the seas that every person on the surface of the planet—every man, woman, and child— will be using some of the same nitrogen atoms that you used in that one Deep Breath.

You may wonder how I know such things. It is simple to deduce, from knowledge of the diffusion of gases and the speeds and habits of the winds, that the thorough mixing will take place. It is also easy to calculate how much air there is on the earth. I could tell it to you in tons, or in the numbers of nitrogen and oxygen atoms, or in terms of breaths. I find that there are three times as many nitrogen atoms in one breath as there are breaths in the whole atmosphere. That means, for example, that every breath of yours at the present time contains, on the average, three of the nitrogen atoms from any given ancient human breath—three atoms, for example, from every one of the breaths that William Shakespeare took throughout his life. The breath that you are just now going to take contains many thousands of the atoms that were used by Shakespeare during the writing of

Hamlet—a wonderful *inspiration* it should be, at least in one sense of that word.

To the same extent, the breath of St. Francis is with us, and of Confucius, and of Mary of Nazareth. That knowledge may give you, I hope, a feeling of brotherhood with the great and holy past, for the nitrogen of the international air crosses the barriers of time as well as space. But each breath of yours, I should hasten to add, contains also nitrogen breathed by ancient sinners; and it probably contains at least six of the nitrogen atoms expelled in each ferocious snort of an ancient dinosaur, as he raised his head from the Mesozoic swamps 100 million years ago and sneered, in his vulgar way, at the primitive little mammals which were just beginning to grow into the most dominant animal form on the earth.

INTERNATIONAL LAW—PHYSICAL

I have dwelled on the subject of human breathing and the spread of breaths in order to emphasize the fact that national boundaries have little significance in man's natural life, or in the discoveries and methods of science. I could have used many other illustrations. The ether waves that carry radio and television broadcasts cross all such boundaries. And the earthquakes of one continent are recorded and studied in all others; they are of international interest because of their bearing on the structure of the earth. The sunlight, the moonlight, the starlight—all fall alike on both sides of national boundary lines.

Let's go back to my first sentence: "Take a deep breath, please. . . ." You sat still, willingly I assume, but with the cooperation of gravity—and that gravitation operates the same in Philadelphia as in Brisbane, in Jamaica as in Cape

Town. Under the impulsion of this same gravitation, apples now fall from trees in Oregon as they fell centuries ago in Isaac Newton's English garden. The laws of genetics and of plant growth are the same in China and in Rhodesia; water freezes according to the same rules in Tasmania and in Alaska.

All this indifference, on the part of natural law, to national boundaries makes it simple and appropriate for us, who study the laws of science, to cooperate internationally. Science is an easy international language. In contrast, working with religious creeds, we are often stopped or hindered by a language barrier or by national boundaries, or because local customs or local politics stand in the way. There is similar blocking at times in political theory and in cultural organization. Music crosses most boundaries, but even Beethoven and Tschaikowsky are less widely understood and appreciated than is the floating of wooden boats on water, or the breeding of domestic animals, or the intricate uses of fire.

To be sure, nationalism is sometimes built up and conditioned by climate, mountains, and oceans. We have national costumes, native songs, domestic architecture, but the nitrogen molecules of the air are the same everywhere: they are international; the sunlight is interplanetary; gravitation is universal.

Let's illustrate internationalism further with an astronomical example. The bright stars of the Southern Cross shine equally on New Zealand, on the Orange Free State, on the Argentine, on all the countries of the Southern Hemisphere. There is no discrimination. Among those stars are some which are continuously radiating messages of special importance to civilized and inquiring mankind. They are, for instance, sending this sort of message: "Our ages are great

[I am quoting the stars], our distances stupendous; the total of time and space, in which you humans on the earth are momentarily involved, is of a magnificance that dwarfs your brief life-span and your space-range to insignificance. But look at us stars again, you humans, and you will see that you are a part of a grander scheme than your prophets of old imagined, for you share with us the laws that rule the galaxies, and share the materials of which they are made. You are made of star stuff. We say to you: 'Man may transcend the inanimate world through his desire and power to comprehend. He can match his mind and spirit against the eternals of space, of time, of cosmic energy; and, with an appropriate balance of pride and humility, he can face fearlessly the cosmic facts, as becomes the high-born animal that he is.' "

That is one message the stars are broadcasting nightly. But more concretely, these stars bring another most fascinating message, of high significance if we can decode it. Some of the stars vary in light intensity. From such variations of starlight we get gradually, after much mental effort, some knowledge of the evolution of stars. From that knowledge we learn gradually, painfully, joyfully, of the probable evolution of our own star, the sun, and the meaning of its place in our galaxy of stars. From this stage in our inquiries we approach knowledge of the origin of our planet and of the other planets of the solar system. Once we have attained some knowledge of the age and origin of our planet, and the story of the formation of its oceans and crystal rocks, we have laid the groundwork for a cosmic view of the development of primitive human biology on the surface of the planet. Step by step, we proceed from star to man—a cosmic evolutionary panorama. That is the message the stars broadcast.

We can get a cosmic view of our own planet if we go

out in space a few million miles. We then appreciate the relation of the planet and animal kingdoms on the Earth to the total of the Earth's surface; we appreciate what an exceedingly thin, superficial part of the planet is available to us—from a mile or two below the surface to ten or fifteen miles above. Just a thin film, available in spots here and there for life—a living film on a moist rocky ball. Satellites and rockets can get a few of us and our instruments higher above the earth's surface; borings, a few miles deeper. But we are essentially superficial.

And also, in imagination, we can back off in time as well as in space, and look at the Earth's plant and animal life as it was ten million years ago, when nothing much like man existed; or a hundred million years ago, when reptiles prevailed and all the kinds of higher mammals were yet unborn; or a thousand million years ago, when very simple plants and animals were slowly evolving at the water's edge.

It was early in the explorable history of the universe that primitive biological forms began using the energy of sunlight. Natural laws were the same then as now. The story of the growth of simple life-forms is but an introduction to the book of knowledge concerning the evolution of the human race. We study these processes of evolution not as Americans, Germans, Australians, Chinese, French, Russians, Norwegians, but as human beings.

Our activities in the sciences, internationally organized, help in laying the groundwork for an interpretation of life. The attack on these deep problems must be international to be effective. It cannot be localized. As life spreads over the whole of the planet, so must the life sciences be worldwide. The winds, the weather, the atmosphere, the ionosphere, the planets, the stars—all must be studied in many countries and cooperatively, to be most successful. The collections of plants and animals, of minerals and the art-work of man, are best studied in those museums where all sections of the world are represented.

Going back to the essentially spiritual endeavor of tracing evolution from star to man, and to the pursuit of science for the sake of knowledge, I should like to point out that we may obtain two important by-products from such scientific work. One by-product is the discovery and development of processes that enrich man's material living—processes such as weather prediction, health protection, radio communication. The second is the bringing of the intellectual people of the various countries together into a common understanding. Understanding—and cooperation.

That word, cooperation, sums up the ethical principle upon which we must base our hopes for man's survival.

Now, with the inspiration of these orienting thoughts on the common breath of mankind and the internationalism of science, let us take up some constructive proposals which may keep us alive and flourishing through the coming decades.

ALTERNATIVES TO EXTINCTION

It may require less than 50 years or it may require more than 200, but optimistically I foresee a civilization covering this planet, sufficiently unified and intelligent to forestall the annihilation of the human race. Before that hoped-for stability arrives, we shall probably suffer some difficult times— even small wars. But the desire to live in an increasingly attractive world is so strong and so widespread that I believe political concessions and life-saving adjustments will be made. Thoughtful planning will be required, however, for thoughtless drifting would be lethal.

First, some remarks on co-existence as national policy. It is already widely operating, and agreeably so, except in the field of socio-economic rivalry between the United States and the U.S.S.R. Differing and inherently antagonistic religious sects co-exist in the majority of the large nations of the world. A dozen or more different nationalities co-exist in Russia (how pleasantly I do not know). Political parties of comparable strength co-exist peacefully, though sometimes noisily, in the United States, Canada, England, Germany and elsewhere.

The socio-economic differences between the U.S.A. and U.S.S.R. seem deep, but they need not permanently menace our modern civilization; both programs appear to work fairly well in their own states. Probably there is as much sincere and passionate grousing against "Party" men in the U.S.S.R. as there is against labor dictators in the U.S.A. Ours is open grousing and apparently not very effective; theirs not so open and possibly more dangerous to the Party. Both political systems, of course, have faults that are more apparent to others than to themselves. We can boast of our free or nearly free press, while we try to minimize the seriousness of our problems of anti-Negro discrimination; the Russians can boast of Sputnik and their intense educational policy, and maintain silence about political prisoners and their unfree press. It is not entirely unrealistic to suggest that we and they may gradually draw nearer together than now— that we both will soften the sharpest antagonisms and learn to appreciate in each other some worthy virtues as well as real and imaginary vices.

How can we attain mutual and peaceful understanding? It is a difficult task: man is naturally combative, and most politicians are naturally greedy for power, prestige, or property. Politics thrives on confusion. Here are, however, a few suggestions bearing specifically on the solving of the U.S.A.-U.S.S.R. problems. Some of the suggested projects could be widely international. When and if needed, similar programs, involving other pairs of nations, could be undertaken—for example, for India and Pakistan, Poland and Germany. But let us attack first the conflict between the U.S.A. and U.S.S.R., for without amelioration and softening of the strain between them, the future could be dark and sudden.

Let us, then, as a beginning:

1. Increase the student interchange until 10,000 visiting students from each nation are continuously involved. This will be expensive, but all-out preparations for or against war are more so. A war could destroy civilization. A massive interchange might save it. Hopefully, the students from neither country would be deliberately brain-washed, either before the exchange or during the residence abroad. Spread the visiting students over the two countries, I suggest, and let natural friendliness do its work of adjustment and mutual understanding.

2. Undertake to extend indefinitely, in several scientific fields, the beautifully working projects of the International Geophysical Year, which brought not only the U.S.A. and U.S.S.R. but more than 60 nations into intensive scientific cooperation. The first trip under the arctic ice, the first man-made satellite, the first moon-approach rocket, the first complete exploration of Antarctica, the discovery of a mysterious radiation belt—these are but five of the accomplishments of the 1957–58 international attack on the problems of the earth as a planet.

3. Inaugurate international "years" in other than geophysical areas. For example: (a) to eliminate the major human, animal, and plant diseases; (b) to study prehistoric man; (c) to construct and exploit deep Plutonic (subterranean) labo-

ratories; (d) to create and distribute new food plants; and (e) to rescue arid lands. To illustrate this last: More than a billion acres of unwatered land, distributed over all the continents, are now lost to mankind. Depending on the future development of cheap atomic energy, we can eventually bring water to all arid areas. To activate such a worldwide project we need heroic international research programs on the inexpensive purifying of salt water, on the developing of edible salt-water vegetation, and on the amelioration of widespread food tabus. We might bring back from the deserts some of the paradises of old, and create new ones.

4. Award decorations, or money prizes, to artists of each other's country, the recipients to be selected by juries mainly from neutral nations. For example, a Tschaikowsky prize to be given by Russia for the best new American symphony or concerto; or a Frank Lloyd Wright award to be made by the United States for the best architectural design or construction in the U.S.S.R.

5. Establish in each other's capitals, and possibly also in each other's largest cities, theater-concert halls devoted in America wholly to Russian productions, classical and modern, and in Russia to American productions. Again an expensive dream, yes—but hate and suspicion are more so, and this educational program could be started modestly.

6. Encourage with cash and applause the present two-way traffic in farmers, artisans, students, artists, and scientists.

The interchange of goods is, of course, important, but not so effective in saving man from his follies as would be the interchange of non-political and non-commercial ideas. Americans and Russians should both always keep in mind that their political and economic inheritances have differed greatly for a long time. All the Russians of age 50 or less —and there are probably more than a hundred million of them—have lived under no other system than that of the present day; why expect them to understand fully and respect our methods and goals? And the 190 million Americans, mostly contented Americans, have lived under no other political system than that which now prevails in America. Little wonder that we worry about other governmental policies than ours. Are we able to understand other systems sympathetically?

The Russians have now and then quietly adopted some "capitalistic" procedures. The Americans have permanently adopted a number of socialistic practices that would have shocked into hysterics the "capitalists" of half a century ago.

"Our system is the right one for the future," says Sam the American; and Ivan the Russian insists: "Our system is the one for the future."

I conclude this argument on a simple ethical note. Born, as we are, of star stuff, we should like to go along with the stars, evolving over the centuries as do they. We have a favorable sun, a dependable planet, an enviable top position in the earth's biology, and the promise of unlimited energy and ease. Good behavior and common sense on an earth-wide scale can take us through the present and future predicaments, if we do not enslave ourselves to slogans and to the futile histories of the past. We do not need to be weak. The two simple mathematical relations,

$$E = Mc^2 \text{ and}$$
$$4\,H = 1\,He + radiation$$

have in them the answer to man's questions about the future —whether he is to continue his evolution into a better life, or is to join the other biological failures as fossils in the dead sedimentary rocks.

8

The One
World of Stars

The sixth President of the United States is credited with the rather astonishing statement that one can judge the culture of a nation by the condition of its astronomical observatories. Unfortunately, John Quincy Adams, whose persistent effort incited his Harvard College to undertake the first ambitious development of astronomical research in America, was succeeded in the White House by men whose devotion to culture did not include active promotion of national efforts to take care of the stars. Their interests were earthy—planetary in scope, or even merely continental. But the thirty-second President (Franklin Roosevelt) took an important part in celebrating the quadricentennial of Copernicus, who was a father of modern science as well as the promulgator of a heliocentric theory of the solar system. Privately F.D.R. expressed whimsically his disagreement with Copernicus: "He looked through the right end of the telescope, thus magnifying his problems. I use the wrong end of the telescope, and it makes things much easier."

Governments and stars have long been associated. In ancient times rulers made use of charlatan astrologers to guide their acts and justify their sins. We now use professors in that role, and investment bankers. The Babylonian, Egyptian, Chaldean, Greek, and Roman cultures supported through their governments astronomical instrumentation, and they ventured interpretations—sometimes using philosophers, sometimes using star-measuring devices.

But the modern coming together of government and astronomy is more significant. The great Royal Observatory in Greenwich was founded by Charles II; the Russian observatory in Pulkovo, which until its destruction in the Second World War held a dominant place in European astronomy, was founded by Czar Nicholas I; Germany's famous observatory at Potsdam was created at the request of the Crown Prince who became Kaiser Friedrich; the Vatican Observatory, located at the Pope's summer residence, is one of the most important of the European astronomical institutions; President Avila Camacho of Mexico personally subsidized and inaugurated the new astrophysical observatory at Tonanzintla, Puebla, where the largest telescope bears his name; and President John Quincy Adams took an outstanding part over a century ago not only in the founding of the Harvard Observatory but also in the dedication of the people's observatory at Cincinnati.

I cannot fully explain why heads of governments in these notable instances have been so keen on astronomical ex-

ploration—why they have been promotive of this most "useless" of human enterprises. Only in small part, I would say,
because of its association with navigation and almanacs, only
in part because of the prestige of its erudite aloofness, and
only in part because of the non-controversial nature of celestial mechanics. Perhaps our primitive ancestors, who were
not bothered by Mazdas and neon lights and were therefore
in closer contact with the stars, had accumulated over the centuries and millennia so much curiosity concerning those
stellar untouchables that for them we continue to discharge
an accumulated responsibility for satisfying curiosity about
heavenly bodies. But these explanations are not complete.
I remain surprised and also, quite naturally, pleased that
astronomy, along with some of the other sciences, is able to
maintain good international relations when economic, religious, and diplomatic intercourse is so very difficult across
national boundaries.

In 1941, when American-Mexican relations were strained
by the confiscation of oil-producing properties and also
strained by politics and by the church-in-education policies
below the Rio Grande, the government of Mexico invited 30
American astronomers to hold a convention in Mexico and
participate in the inauguration of a new observatory. This
astronomical gambit was followed in succeeding years by
expeditions into Mexico (again under Mexican government
auspices and expense) of physicists and mathematicians.

ASTRONOMICAL COOPERATION

The first international scientific congress after World War II
was held in Moscow in 1945 by the Russian, Scandinavian,
English, American, Indian, and other astronomers. Was this

conference permitted by suspicious governments because astronomers are harmless, or because they are convincingly devoted to non-nationalism in science?

Nine Russian astronomers spent many months in the United States in 1947, visiting all the observatories and taking part in conferences. Later the U.S.S.R Academy of Sciences invited the International Astronomical Union to hold its next worldwide conferences in Leningrad—an invitation which was of course welcomed, because a score of Russian astronomers were on the international astronomical commissions and one of them was vice-president of our international astronomical union.

Apparently the sun, moon, and stars ride high above the nation-separating curtains. In meteorology, agriculture, geodesy, and in special branches of medicine the famous curtain has been penetrated. It is a net which tangles operations somewhat, but with patience and persistence the obstructions set up by politicians and statesmen are bypassed or overflown, and the natural two-way traffic in good will and cooperation continues.

The "One World of Stars" is, in fact, a reality, and its significance should not be ignored in other fields of science and art. One-worldness need not be confined to the cultural fields. The stars are supranational, as also are the laws of gravitation, genetics, radiation, nutrition. Cannot good will, human brotherhood, and a common ambition for the higher cultures also develop as boundary passers?

Let us discuss the internationalism of some major astronomical adventures and show how international collaboration is essential for the progress of the science, and in these nervous days doubly important for the progress of international amity.

The twenty-fourth president of the American Association for the Advancement of Science was Simon Newcomb. Somewhat incidentally he was a novelist, an economist, and a government official, but primarily he was a mathematical astronomer and one of the most renowned American scientists of the nineteenth century. One of his early studies concerned the positions and motions of the sun, moon, and planets. He sought to bring order out of the chaos resulting from much uncoordinated measurement in the many national observatories. Jupiter and Saturn are rather obstreperous in the way they pull and push around the smaller planets, ours included. But by using all the old and modern measures of their positions, Newcomb and his assistants, after cleaning the observations properly, could develop theories to predict accurately just where the planets would be in the years to come.

It is definitely an international job—this refined study of planetary motions—and in 1871 we find Newcomb in Germany looking up the old records and then in France digging into the century-old archives to find the observations made by gone and forgotten observers. At the Paris Observatory he worked diligently on the stars and planets, which are the property of all nations, and he remained essentially oblivious of the cannonading the French were then using to settle a political question.

Going farther back, we recall that in 1780 the British military governor of the Penobscot Bay area gave permission to the representatives of the American Academy of Arts and Sciences and of Harvard University to go to the Maine coast for the observation of a total eclipse of the sun. Although the Americans and British were at this time busy with the Revolutionary War, this astronomical enterprise seemed to be worthy, and arrangements for the trip were easily made.

The available maps, by the way, were faulty, and the observers missed the totality by locating their station at the southern edge of the eclipse path. But the expedition was not a failure. In a nice demonstration of serendipity, the astronomers, through this accident of a wrong location, observed something more interesting than the solar corona they had journeyed far to see. The Rev. Samuel Williams, the Harvard professor of natural philosophy, saw for the first recorded time the brilliant beads of light that frequently appear just as an eclipse is beginning or ending its total phase. These bright flares result from sunlight pouring through the deep mountain valleys on the moon's edge. The eclipse "beads," first noted in Revolutionary-War time, were described again 50 years later by an Englishman and are now unfairly known by his name. They are called Baily's beads instead of Williams' beads, as they should be in the name of justice. But the American astronomers are not inclined to make an international incident of the matter. They are not asking His Majesty's Government whom the devil they think they are pushing around.

In fact, astronomers and other scientists are not natural war-makers. Their real fights are against unknowns, not against neighbors. Scientists' problems are worldwide problems. There is no place for selfish nationalism in astronomy or medicine, in mathematics or meteorology. What one scientist discovers becomes the property of the world of science and the world of all men.

At least, that is ideally true. In practice, in a society of free enterprise, many scientific discoveries in physics and chemistry are not free to *all* men. The discoveries become trade secrets and are developed for private profit, and only eventually for "all men." As business secrets, the discoveries and developments are not open to inspection by rivals in business, or by the United Nations. Our own American system of exploiting the fruits of science thus points to the difficulty of establishing international inspection.

Another illustration that science and man's interests in science transcend war hatreds and operate to decrease national prejudices is well-known. During his famous travels of scientific discovery in the late eighteenth century, the renowned English navigator, Captain James Cook, was protected by the American government, through the agency of Benjamin Franklin, from the American privateers that then roamed the ocean and harassed British shipping.

During World War II the astronomers maintained a sort of impersonal contact across or around the battle lines. I remember, for instance, that a Russian astronomer at his observatory south of the Caucasus on the Turkish frontier in Asia discovered a new comet. The German armies were overrunning western and southern Russia, and terrible battles were in progress in the northern Caucasus. The discovery of the comet was radioed across the battle lines to Moscow, and Moscow found time and interest to radio it directly to the Harvard Observatory for further telegraphic distribution.

Also during the war, in Rumania, which was an ally of Germany at the time, a comet was discovered and reported to the Rumanian Royal Astronomer in Bucharest, who reported it to the Danish Royal Astronomer in Copenhagen, who transmitted it to the Chief Astronomer in Switzerland, who forwarded it to America. The United States Navy, by the way, checked up on this Rumanian comet rather carefully to see if it was subversive.

EROS AND THE SOLAR PARALLAX

Not only in reporting astronomical events, but also in prolonged researches, astronomers continue to demonstrate the One World of Stars. There is a striking recent story of cooperation which should be recorded: namely, the new and most accurate measurement of the distance from the earth to the sun—the solar parallax.

This distance is the so-called "astronomical unit," approximately 93 million miles in length. It is a fundamental unit for measurements throughout the extraterrestrial universe. The ancient Greeks tried to estimate the distance to the sun, with little success, and during the eighteenth and nineteenth centuries much attention was given to the various ways, direct and indirect, of finding the solar parallax.

Direct measures of the sun's distance from the surface of the earth are clumsy. Since all the distances between all the bodies in the solar system are linked together through gravitation, it has been found best to operate indirectly by measuring the distances of the planets from each other and deducing from them the solar distance. A small, rapidly moving planet has advantages in this research, and therefore much attention has turned, since its discovery half a century ago, to the asteroidal planet Eros, which is periodically brought, in its somewhat elongated orbit, very near the earth. The sharpness of asteroidal images on the photographic plates occasionally permits a precision of measurement not attained in measuring objects of large angular diameter, such as the sun and the moon.

About 18 miles in diameter, this asteroid Eros is not ordinary. Most of the 1,500 tabulated minor planets stay on their reservation between the orbits of Mars and Jupiter.

But Eros and a few other small ones follow cometlike orbits, and occasionally through nearness they give astronomers the opportunity of making highly precise measures of motion and position. These minor planets, although merely fragments, accurately obey the planetary laws of motion; therefore they reveal, after much analysis, the distances separating earth and sun, moon and earth, and the other planetary separations. As a by-product, the analysis of the measures of Eros gives us a determination of the mass of the moon.

In 1931 Eros and terrestrial astronomers had one of their occasional get-togethers—a separation of only 16 million miles. We knew about the coming nearness long in advance. In 1928 the astronomers of the world had met in Holland and made detailed plans for the 1931 "opposition." Many observations should be made of many reference stars in many countries. Thirty-six observatories on five continents took part. No one thought it necessary to explain the plan to the diplomats or even mention what was going on. A special committee examined the possibilities and made assignments. From Australia to Canada, from Argentina to Sweden, from the Japanese Royal Observatory to the Harvard station on the Modder River near Bloemfontein, Orange Free State, we did our work at the appointed times.

The famous spectrum expert, Annie J. Cannon of the Harvard Observatory, classified on a special series of photographs the spectra of the stars that would be used to compare with Eros as it hurried through the star fields. Where it would travel we had roughly predicted, but to improve the parallax of the sun we had to plot Eros' path with the highest possible precision, and the colors of the stars deduced from Miss Cannon's spectrum classifications would have a bearing on the precision possible from micrometer settings. Eros is yellowish, and we would get into trouble with refraction and other difficulties if its position was derived from comparisons with deep red stars or those peculiarly blue.

After a few weeks of its juxtaposition in 1931, Eros went on about its business, becoming too faint and far away to interest astronomers further, but the few weeks of observation had given us thousands of measures. The prolonged labor of deducing the parallax lay ahead. The measures, by international arrangement, were sent to His Majesty's Astronomer at the Cape of Good Hope (later the Astronomer Royal of England), Sir Harold Spencer-Jones. To him had been assigned the heavy job of analysis.

The micrometric measures of Eros from 15 observatories entered the final determinations of the parallax. Leipzig, Greenwich, and Berlin took important observing assignments. They completed their work before all interchange between Britain and Germany degenerated, in 1939, into murderous bombs and propaganda. Finally, in 1941, at the height of the world's worst war, in which maddened, frightened nations were trying at great expense of human life and wealth to destroy each other, the British Astronomer Royal calmly announced that the best value of the solar distance, thanks to the international cooperation of scientists, was 93,-005,000 miles, with an uncertainty of only 8,000 miles. The new value of the solar parallax was not greatly different from the values previously determined, but the uncertainty of the determination had been reduced to a twenty-fifth of the earlier uncertainty. The new value was, of course, immediately communicated to the scientists of all the warring nations.

Human knowledge of a "constant" of nature had gained through cooperative internationalism. But who gained, and what did they gain, by the concurrent bitter hates of nationalism and by the slaughters of the science-engulfing war? The war could not have been avoided, you say. Perhaps the eccentricity of the orbit of Eros needs international cooperation less than do the eccentricities of human behavior.

THE CORONAGRAPH

The One World of Stars could be more extensively illustrated, but I have chosen only a few modern incidents which particularly demonstrate new techniques in astronomy and show the necessity or advisability of international collaboration.

The sun is an international power plant and plays no favorites. Solar astronomers the world over began active collaboration 50 years ago. They set up central bureaus for the recording of solar phenomena. Special observatories for the study of the sun have now been established in India, California, northern Chile, France, Colorado, Michigan, Switzerland, Austria, Holland, Russia, and elsewhere. Some of the observations are reported daily through a telegraphic interchange, because certain phenomena associated with the sun operate swiftly, and they influence, in a significant fashion, the ionospheric layers of the earth's atmosphere.

The sun brings together not only different countries but also the different sciences. The problems of its radiation unite the botanist and the astronomer, the cosmologist and the physicist, the paleontologist and the weather man. The sun has inspired the religions of primitive men, and its transmutation of atoms of matter into energy of radiation inspires the utmost in modern technology. The sun is indeed the guiding light to the atomic age.

But we know so little about the sun—its spots, its spicules, its prominences, and corona. To solve such mysteries, the combined efforts of all astrophysicists are needed. Let's start our exposition with the corona, the ethereal high atmosphere of the sun, which we used to be able to see only during the total eclipses, because the faint coronal glow is lost in the glare of full sunlight. An ingenious young French astronomer, Bernard Lyot, some 30 years ago began to solve the problem of examining the elusive corona at leisure. He installed an eclipse-producing moon (special diaphragm) inside his telescope. He did it so carefully that his "coronagraph," set up on a high mountain above the earth's layer of dust—on Pic du Midi in southern France—concealed the solar disk and brought out the faint coronal light.

Following and modifying Lyot's technique, Donald H. Menzel and Walter O. Roberts of the Harvard Observatory built the first coronagraph of the Western Hemisphere. It is located high in the Rocky Mountains at Climax, Colorado, and has been operated under the joint auspices of Harvard and the University of Colorado. It records daily the corona and its changing intensity, and it also records, with proper accessory apparatus, the solar prominences. Those hot solar clouds change form from hour to hour, some explosively and some slowly. The coronagraph permits the making of continuous pictures—one exposure every half minute, for example. When these exposures are properly assembled and speeded up, we have a motion picture of the mighty gas storms on the surface of this nearby and typical star of ours. The speeds of the solar motions are 3,000 to 4,000 times the speed of the winds in our earth's atmosphere.

It is of interest to record that the solar explosions are internationally studied—observationally and theoretically.

American, French, Swedish, English, Australian, German, Austrian, and Russian scientists are working on these problems, in part because of their basic scientific interest and in part because the various solar radiations, operating at long distance on the earth's atmosphere, affect radio transmission, the Northern Lights, the magnetic needle, and possibly to some extent our weather. The solar corona is still something of a mystery, especially its astonishing temperature, which may be something like a million degrees C., although the surface of the sun it surrounds has a temperature of only 6,000° C.

The chemical composition of the material in the solar corona, for 60 years a mystery, appears at last to be solved, and again the boundaries between nations were ignored. Following ideas and intimations provided by many spectroscopists, especially the work of the German astrophysicist W. Grotrian, Dr. B. Edlén, a young Swedish physicist, has come out with the astonishing theory that the airy, scintillating corona of the sun owes its chief radiation to atoms of heavy elements. Before the work of Grotrian and Edlén, scientists generally believed that the corona must be composed of very light elements, but now we find that the excited atoms of iron, nickel, and calcium provide most of the radiation. These atoms are highly ionized. Their outer electrons have been blown away by the excessive radiations, or by whatever it is that excites so violently and ionizes so fully these common heavy elements in the upper atmosphere of the sun.

We must learn more about this business, because what works on the sun doubtless works on the billions of stars of our Milky Way galaxy. And we shall learn more, if we keep out of a civilization-ruining war, because the scientists of a dozen nations are turning their mathematical, observational, and interpretational skills to the question: How did that iron get into the rare upper solar atmosphere, and what is agitating it so excitedly that the excitement crosses 93 million miles of space and disturbs our terrestrial radios?

THE WANDERING OF THE POLES

The Second World War, which we fought to preserve freedom and civilization, and doubtless for other reasons, did pretty badly by scientific civilization in many countries, especially interrupting the energetic and ambitious Japanese scientists. In a devastated and vanquished country, the surviving scientific laboratories and observatories usually are not prosperous. We record, however, one exception in Japan. Before the war there was in that country a kindly old gentleman who was recognized the world over as the leader in a certain phase of geodesy—in the highly organized international enterprise called "The Study of the Variation of Latitude." Dr. Hisashi Kimura was the chairman of an international commission involving geodesists of a dozen nations. To this commission had been assigned, by scientists and governments, the job of keeping track of the wandering of the poles of the earth. The true latitude of a place is its angular distance from the equator, or 90° minus its distance from the North Pole. It is a constant, of course, if the Pole stays put; but that is just what the North Pole does not do. For reasons that I shall not outline, because they are complicated and in part unknown, the Pole wanders erratically over an area about the size of a large lecture hall. If you should sometime go to the North Pole and want to place a flag or carve your initials, you should make your observations of position precise and act quickly, or the Pole will be elsewhere.

Of course we do not need to go to the Pole to study these wanderings. We can set up an observatory almost anywhere, and with continuous observations of a special sort, on stars in or near the zenith, we can check up on the unsteadiness. To do it right, however, several observatories are needed. The stations must be, for the best effect, in different longitudes and preferably all on the same latitude circle. Years ago a network of five specialized observatories was set up, one each in Italy, southern Russia, Japan, California, and Maryland. The observations in Italy and the United States were seriously interrupted during the Second World War, but they were maintained continuously in Russia and Japan.

After the death of Dr. Kimura, an Italian took over the coordinating responsibilities, and the four united nations—united in geodesy, that is—continue to trace the wanderings of the Pole and measure the variations of latitude, which are apparently caused by internal and superficial changes in our earth. Here again it is as though there were an international mind that wants to know about the intricacies of the physical world and, to attain its goal, hopes not to be bothered by national boundaries.

$E = mc^2$

My story of the One World of Stars goes all the way from the wobbles of the axis of one planet, making annual trips around one star, to the total of all stars and the space-time in which they are involved.

When Albert Einstein began to write his epoch-making theories, he was building directly on the mathematical explorations of Russian, German, Italian, Irish, and other mathematicians. The world-mind of mathematical physics was at work on the basic problems of the nature of the universe. National vanity, racial prestige, and stupid human strife were irrelevant.

The famous relativity theory, it was soon learned, could best be verified by astronomical tests. At the end of the First World War, while the generals and diplomats wrangled, British astronomers under the guidance of Sir Arthur Eddington went off on a hazardous eclipse expedition to test the accuracy of a German's prediction about the bending of light at the edge of the sun. Some of the formidable equations of the relativistic cosmogonies were solved by the Russian Alexander Friedman, the Belgian Georges Lemaître, and the Americans H. P. Robertson and R. C. Tolman.

The most famous little equation in the world, $E = mc^2$, developed out of Einstein's early work just at the time astronomers needed it to help account for the obviously long life of the sun. The equation showed that the stars feed on themselves. Their matter gradually melts into radiation. Atomic energy is released in the sun at just the right rate, through the building of hydrogen into helium. Thus it has been for a few billion years, and so it will likely be for a few trillion years more.

Already, at the turn of the century the atomic age was budding. For the astronomers it was in full bloom long before the splitting sensation of uranium 235. Fission and fusion were international discoveries participated in by scientists of a dozen nations. The One World of Atoms was demonstrated as clearly as the world unity of astronomy, of biology, and of chemical reactions.

We can now build and split atoms in our laboratories,

but there is nothing we can do with the galaxies—those gigantic, wheel-shaped star systems that are strewn by the millions throughout the recently discovered outer spaces. Nor can we do anything with those smaller sidereal systems, the beautiful globular clusters, except to study them and learn of their enormous populations of giant stars; measure their times, energies, positions, and motions; guess at their origins and destinies; and bring back to the philosophies and religions of men the raw materials useful in the new world of knowledge and intellectual opportunity.

Some great spiral galaxies are probably similar in form to the one in which we are located. Others are irregular, like the nearby clouds of Magellan, to which the Harvard Observatory has paid much attention for the past 50 years. Still other galaxies are spheroidal and symmetrical, looking much like supergiant globular clusters, which indeed they may be.

Sometime ago about 40 of us (from a dozen countries) who were particularly interested in the problems of galaxies, met in Zurich, Switzerland, to talk over the questions demanding further study. It was a truly international gathering. The goal was the solution of difficult problems. There was little or no jockeying for national prestige, no belittling of small observatories, no struts about manifest destinies and national aspirations. It was an assembly of those who represented a unified world curiosity, a unified desire to understand the universe, a united front in a special battle against our common enemy, ignorance.

In our conference it became clear that we need additional observations to test the existing theories about the nature of space, time, and the expanding universe, and we need more theory to interpret some of the newer surprise observations which do not fit into currently acceptable patterns. We want the 200-inch telescope to tell us more about the speed of recession of the galaxies heretofore too remote for spectrum analysis; we want the new Schmidt-type reflectors to increase observationally the stability of our census of the whole metagalaxy, through searching out the millions of individual galaxies that are within reach.

AN INTERNATIONAL INSTRUMENT

From the Baker-Schmidt telescope in South Africa—which started as a joint enterprise of Eire, the United States, and North Ireland—we need more detailed information on the nucleus of our own galaxy. This powerful new-type instrument is now operated by six northern observatories—truly international. It is mounted on Harvard Kopje in the Orange Free State, and there it is in a strategic location, with the hub of our wheel-shaped galaxy passing conveniently every day directly overhead. It joins in finding answers to some of the pressing questions about the nature of our galaxy and of galaxies in general.

It is fitting that these basic researches on the nature of the physical world are undertaken with the aid of an internationally owned and operated instrument. The most valuable written document in the Harvard archives, it seems to me, is the agreement between the Dunsink Observatory of the Government of Eire, the Armagh Observatory of the Archbishopric of North Ireland, and the Harvard Observatory which set up the South African telescope. This document is a simple statement, but its importance lies in the fact that it was jointly signed by the Catholic Bishop of Dublin and the Protestant Archbishop of Armagh, North Ireland—a document unique in history, I believe, and symbolic of the willingness and desire, when led by the stars, to cooperate across religious and political boundaries.

Here we have revealed, it may be, a prime function of science, and of the American Association for the Advancement of Science as it enters its second century. Cooperation across national boundaries is so simple and effective in the sciences that we have a clear responsibility to lead the way into an era of peace and human progress, without which our efforts for human knowledge and human comforts will have been in vain. Our species of man, the sapient one, is now at one of its critical epochs. Will it survive the crisis through the use of intelligence and the submersion of avarice, or will it join the fossil biological failures of the past, which, through inability to meet their crises, ceased long ago to greet nightly the world of enduring stars?

9

Science and Non-Science

We humans are generally very astute in scientific research and in technical applications. Usually we are careful and rational when we deal with things we see and hear and facts we record. However, being human, we are also often happily gullible. And when we are in that gullible mood, we are prone to take non-science seriously—flying saucers, for example.

Now one basic principle of scientific investigation is that before a fact can be safely deduced from a measurement—from a reading on a voltmeter, for instance, or from a mathematical computation—the measurement or computation must be repeated, preferably in a somewhat different way. It must be checked.

Measures and verbal descriptions have inescapable errors, because our tools and our logic are not perfect. It is fundamental that we must verify our results, set up controls, have respect for the cause-and-effect relationships, and not throw out discordant measures or neglect adverse observations.

The really important measurements are sometimes those that do not agree with other measurements or with some guiding theory. The cause of the deviation should be sought. The deviations tell us sometimes that the methods we have been using are faulty. Sometimes they help us to identify factors we had thought would not be involved. Such disagreeing observations have occasionally led to brilliant discoveries—and they have also served to kill many a rash theory.

The basic difference between science and non-science is that truly scientific work is permeated by objectivity. The true scientist seeks true answers and cares not (while he is working as a scientist) whether his results are pleasant or unpleasant. As a social being he may be happier about pleasant and fruitful discoveries, but as a scientist he wants knowledge, regardless.

A non-scientist preoccupied with flying saucers, or astrology, or tea-leaf fortune telling, or water dowsing, too often seeks answers that best fit his personal theory or wish. He is likely to "doctor" his measures in order to get the results desired. He thinks he knows the answer before he makes the experiment. Too often he will say: "I am going to prove my theory." He should, of course, say: "I want to test my theory, and if the test is positively against it, out goes the theory."

FLYING SAUCERS

Let us examine some of the places where science is beclouded by non-science, and by its offspring, superstition. As said above, we are occasionally very gullible. Consider the willingness of some to believe in flying saucers as something supernatural, to believe incredible things, to ignore basic scientific principles and embrace the totally irrational.

I myself have seen many flying saucers—objects, that is, which are widely accepted as mysterious phenomena. They are genuine enough as phenomena, even if not as saucers. For example, I know of seven types that can be and have been reported with more or less astonishment as flying saucers:

Stratospheric aircraft.
Weather balloons.
Searchlights playing on broken cloud fields.
Slow-moving meteorites, sometimes called fireballs.
Atmospheric mirages.
Hallucinations.
Vapor trails of high-flying jet planes.

All of these are real and rational, even the hallucinations. We know their origins. No mystery about them. Natural laws govern them. Nothing supernatural. Nothing from Mars or Venus.

A fertile source of "saucer" reports is the weather balloon. It carries aloft instruments to record air pressures, winds, temperatures, and so on, at various altitudes. Equipped with a small radio transmitter, these soaring balloons become midget broadcasting stations, telemetering their records to receiving stations on the earth. The balloons, once released, are usually not recaptured; they drift and ascend until the reduction of pressure in the upper air causes them to burst. Seeing such an object drifting in the sunlight, the scientific man seeks an explanation. He asks: "What sort of object might be aloft at this time which would explain my observation?" The possible causes are considered, sorted, evaluated. That is the scientific method.

In contrast, the non-scientific observer grabs at the most exciting explanation and produces bizarre accounts of interplanetary visitors, or something equally foolish.

The best flying saucers I have seen were caused by an airfield searchlight playing on a broken cloud field. These wandering, dashing, fading spots of light, with no visible connection to the ground, go through all the strange antics attributed to flying saucers, except that they fail to produce little green men crawling out of spaceship windows and speaking broken Yiddish!

The craters on the moon were mostly produced by falling meteorites. These small bodies even now collide at high speed with the planets and moons, our own included. The large ones (fireballs), moving faster than a jet plane through the earth's night or twilight sky, incite highly emotional reactions in those minds that are mystery-filled and prone to believe in flying saucers. We know, however, that these fireballs have an interplanetary origin; they are relatively rare, certainly are unmanned, and most of them burn themselves out before reaching the earth's surface.

We are all familiar with the oiled-road mirage—a common heat effect. There are also atmospheric mirages. These are caused by an abnormal layer of air high above the earth's surface, which reflects what is below according to the simple optics of a mirror. Such a mirage moves with the observer, just as do the ends of the rainbow.

The illusion and hallucination types of flying saucers are products often of the weary, or confused, or excited mind of the observer. You can sometimes be talked into believing the illusions of others. You believe as a fact what you want to be a fact. I recall a famous subscriber to what we might call the flying-saucer illusion. You remember Hamlet's spoofing at the expense of Polonius? Hamlet asks:

"Do you see that cloud that's almost in shape like a camel?"

Polonius replies: "By the mass, and it's like a camel, indeed."

Hamlet: "Methinks it is like a weasel."

Polonius: "It is backed like a weasel."

Hamlet: "Or like a whale?"

Polonius: "Very like a whale."

Polonius should write a book on flying saucers.

No one would call Polonius a realist, but there is no doubt about his sobriety. When it comes to flying saucers, however, some realists report that they can see saucers best when in their cups.

ASTROLOGICAL HOKUM

One of the most remarkably persistent frauds to be perpetrated on a rather intelligent and partly-educated society is the Astrology column, carried daily by numerous newspapers. It is "Your daily activity-guide according to the stars." To develop a message for today, you are advised to read words corresponding to numbers of your Zodiac birth sign. Suppose the birthday is in mid-December. According to the ritual of astrology, this day is marked by the sign of Sagittarius. It is supposed to have properties described as bicorporal—hot and dry. Decoding the message for those "crossed" by such a sign, the astrologer finds that: "The tide is with you in raising cash." There is a remote possibility that by chance someone will find this true for himself, but you will certainly not find any connection in logic between the message, the numerals, the stars in the constellation Sagittarius, and cash. It is, of course, buncombe!

Astrology claims to be based on "forces" exerted by the planets and stars. No professional astronomer, at present or in the past hundred years, has believed in these claims. The astronomers, scientists of the sky, know of nothing in the laws of gravitation or magnetism, or any other natural law, that would suggest such "forces"—no scientific justification for astrology.

As an astronomer I am sometimes asked: "But isn't there really *something* in astrology, something valuable?" "Sure," I say ungrammatically, "there is indeed something in astrology—a good many millions a year paid by dupes to the charlatans who trade in superstitions. Quite a good business it is. Probably much more is spent on astrological hokum than on astronomy."

Subscribers to astrology are, I believe, typical of all those who subscribe to irrational prediction: they remember and talk about the successes, if any, and forget those predictions that do not come off. As mentioned above, astronomy makes good use of its failures; non-science does not. The policy of forgetting failure is essential to all branches of occult interpretation and prediction. Forgetting failures is especially prevalent among psychic operators, astrologers, medical quacks, and amateur weathermen. It is essential to their business success.

"Things have gone fine with me since I began to carry this

rabbit's foot," says your neighbor, thus giving more credit to a dismembered dead rabbit than to his own ability to manage things. We all fall in one way or other for this sort of irrational magic: horseshoes over the door, salt over the shoulder, potatoes planted at the time of the waning moon. If things go adversely, we don't blame the faltering "protection" but look for some other occult reason for our hard luck.

Beliefs in magic are a part of our folklore, and much of it is associated with weather observation and prediction, some of which is not unscientific but is based on repeated observations. For example, there is a good deal of reliability in the homely warning:

Red at night, sailors' delight;
Red in the morning, sailors take warning.

Red skies do offer us reasonable predictions. One authority puts it this way: "A red evening sky means that the temperature has not fallen below the dewpoint, even at the tops of the strongly cooled rising currents of air that are so common during the heated portion of the afternoon, and hence the air contains so little moisture that rain, within the coming 24 hours, is improbable." Metereological knowledge also shows that red skies in the morning represent a different condition which may produce stormy weather. In other words, the jingle makes scientific sense.

But our folklore contains some weather non-science as well. When the crescent moon is lying on its back, it is supposed to hold water, which is interpreted in one version to mean that the water will spill out and give us a rainy spell—and in another, equally positive version, to mean that the crescent will *hold* the water and therefore that we are in for a dry spell. This, in credulous disregard of the facts that the moon is spherical, is completely free of air and water, is a quarter of a million miles beyond the rain clouds of our atmosphere, and looks exactly the same from the stormy North Atlantic as from the dust bowls of the Southwest.

The only detectable effects of the moon on the earth are gravitational (as shown by the tides in waters, land and air) and in luminosity (as shown by its reflection of sunlight— that is, by moonshine). The orientation of the new moon crescent depends on the relative positions of the earth, the sun, and the moon. These are known decades in advance from astronomical calculations. Obviously the orientation of the moon's crescent has no measurable correlation with the weather.

When it comes to fanciful weather predictions, an old but quite faithless friend is the *Old Farmer's Almanack*. Its predictions are meant to be humorous, and sometimes they are. The predictions for a year in advance are the same for rainy Seattle and the rainless Death Valley, the same for the monsoon region of India and the Sahara Desert. For example, here is a typical autumn forecast for the whole of North America, made months ahead: "Normal, including gales, but not hurricanes north of the Carolinas. September 1 to 15, cold and fine; 17 to 24, gales, but hurricanes stay down south; 25 to 30, cools off. October 1 to 4, fine; 5 to 7, storms; 8 to 20, wonderful; 24 to 31, snow flurries."

This can be taken all in fun. "Nonsense" is here the right word, not non-science; and this world of ours is so grim at times that we should welcome a bit of nonsense now and then.

Take note, though, that there is no similarity between the *Farmer's Almanack* and the very sober United States Nautical Almanac, which contains tables of the accurately predicted positions of stars and planets. The latter is published by the Government for the use of astronomers and navigators. It has nothing to do with weather prediction, which is the province of the United States Weather Bureau and the aircraft companies.

WATER DOWSING

One non-science much practiced and widely believed in—water witching, or water dowsing with a "divining rod"—is rather pathetic. The pathos is that so many fairly judicious people are taken in by it. The forked willow twig in a dowser's hands defies scientists, common sense, and the laws of nature. "It works!" they say. (*They*, of course, overlook failures.) We have heard that army colonels have sometimes used the "professional" dowser to locate water for a camp, but to my mind that does not necessarily commend the practice or insure its truth.

In the hands of the "right people," a dowsing twig, when successful, seems to meet the scientific requirement of repeatability—that is, by the right people. As a matter of fact, I myself am a pretty good operator with the forked twig. I have some dowsing twigs that completely overcome my resistance, overpower my hands, and point to water sources—whenever I *want* them to! If you cut your twig in the dark of the moon, grease it with 'possum oil, have confidence, and prepare to forget your failures, it will work for you every time. Once I had a dowsing twig cut under a waxing moon from an apple tree growing beside a graveyard; it was supersensitive! Ignoring the nearby Charles River, it located a pint bottle of bourbon in a friend's hip pocket! What strange science do you suppose was there involved—chemical, electrical, psychological, or something wonderful beyond our understanding?

10

Science and the
Humanistic Tradition

Today's science is, we acknowledge, a jealous taskmaster. It is
often inimical to soft hours of leisure for traditional learning.
It is intolerant of the careless approximations of art, and of
the prejudices that soil attempts at social interpretations. It
wearies of the weak introversions that pervert analyses of
spirit. And therefore, unless carefully watched, science drives
its practitioners away from the book shelves and the art
galleries, and away from the communal firesides where human chatter so often builds the soul and goals of civilization.

The scientists are driven into the laboratories, and to their
drawing boards and technical handbooks, not only by devotion to science but also by the firm conviction that human
destiny now depends on their creations and on their integrity

to the last possible decimal place. And of course they are right in that conviction. Which leaves me personally in a quandary. Why should I appear in a conference on the Humanistic Tradition? Non-science is hardly the field for a scientist.

CONFLICT AND CHOICE

My history must be similar to that of many scientists. My reason for entering a university was chiefly to prepare for a literary career! Strange how wildly ambitious and futile the young can be in spite of the cruel lessons of history! But soon, in my illusions of that day, I saw hypocrisy and dishonesty in professional journalism, pretense and femininity in song and essay. In contrast, the solidity and sincerity of planetary rotation and revolution were highly attractive to one submerged in ignorance—his own and the race's. Prediction followed by fulfillment was appealing, then as now.

The humanities did have their harmonies, of course, and occasionally their measurable structures. But the mathematical metrics of poetry, as in a translation I made of Catullus, had more attraction than the sensations of heart or spleen that were depicted in the arguments of the poems. The cycles outshone the sentiment. Nevertheless, my first or second juvenility in the realm of undergraduate scholarship was a combination of classics and science.

With me the classics were at a disadvantage. The neat allure in mathematical formulae revealed beauties that an epode could not attain; the statements about optics by Archimedes provided intellectual comforts and thrills that Raphael's approximations to human faces and forms could not equal.

And, on the practical side, the challenge held out by the

sciences, and the secrets their study might resolve, seemed to promise happier returns than those attainable through the rethinking of old thoughts and the warming over of ideas that had been repeatedly warmed. Reaching for the stars surpassed toying with the literatures. In consequence, the garlands of the classical poets were long ago pressed into my memory book, along with the sad flowers of adolescent days, and I now get my Latin inscriptions translated by some convenient schoolboy.

It has been an unhappiness for me, and doubtless for many other scientists, to discover that the native impulse to write with free and careless abandon has been rigidly cramped into the dull, word-thrifty conciseness of the routine scientific report. Where once we were blithe and gay in expressing an idea, we now move sedately down conventional ruts. No longer do we decorate our phrases with ambiguous subtleties. The aromas of yesterday's reading or last night's dreams are out of place in the report on "The Latitude Frequency of Dwarf Second-Type Binaries." The whippoorwills are absent from the Geiger-Müller counters, and there are no butterflies with azure-tipped wings alight on the integral signs. Color is gone from the microwaves, also from the description of wiring circuits for control panels.

Moreover, if color and free-wheeling charm were not absent from his scientific writing, the scientist would soon fade from the respect of colleagues. Science strives to be exact, and economical. It is already too difficult for easy grasp by over-tired minds, and small sympathy have we for those who would fuzz up science with disorderly thinking and the artistic garnishment of non-science.

However restrained he may be in practical writing, the scientist is not stopped from high admiration of good composition. Artistry in criticism, and ability to criticize, impel his admiration. My scientific friends seem to share with me a wistful respect for literary scholarship, and they have as lively an appreciation of the graphic arts and music as the non-scientific of my acquaintance. Charles Darwin complained of his declining interest in art and music as his scientific life developed. But his loss may have been indicative of the temperament of an individual and not of the class; moreover, there is in his own scientific prose something which habitually puts it, in spite of the great wisdom of its themes, into anthologies alongside the work of literary artists who often wrote in fine ignorance of their subject matter.

In addition to the stylistic cramping that forces the natural scientist away from the graces of literature, and in addition to the necessities of his work, which direct his study of language into practical linguistics rather than the appreciation of foreign literatures, the scientist is further conditioned by his trade. He is likely to find himself intolerant of the easy though entertaining introversion that is a fellow-traveler of the Humanistic Tradition. Objectivity becomes something of a fetish with the scientist, and he is likely to grow sharply impatient with the introspective humanist.

For example, when a vain artist, working in words or notes or oils, insists that he puts his soul into his production, the scientist unkindly observes that the artist is egotistically uttering nonsense. The equation of soul cannot be written. Soul cannot even be defined clearly, or described. The egocentric artist takes himself, of all things, seriously; he puts his own triviality out of balance and perspective. He looks neither back to the fossil bones of his mammalian progenitors nor forward to the galactic rotations. In his obsession with self, with a transient, trivial self, with his own mess of matter temporarily alive, he seeks to impose on his contemporaries an expression of what he presumes to be his own individuality. He tries to market some hypothetical aura which, he assumes, miraculously hovers around his body, around his allotment of nitrogenous compounds. He seeks to express in words, notes, lines, or colors, the so-called spirit associated with his own assortment of chemical elements.

Fortunately he fails. He fools himself about his own unique self-expression. For he is not only himself. He is not an isolated entity. If, beyond training and technical skill, he expresses anything of note from his spiritual innards, it comes from the complicated nerve-associated inheritance of a long line of anthropoids, salps, worms, and primitive protozoa. He expresses the biotic lineage; and that is as it should be, for unknowingly he ties in the human race with the cosmos, temporarily if not spatially. He makes a culminating exhibition of the organic processes that have been transmitted across the ages. That is fine and encouraging, because our artists, in a broad sense, are the top of human civilization, representing the goal toward which we strive in our struggle to differentiate our species from what we like to call the lower organisms. The artist's aura is also ours, his "soul" a fragment of the vague "over-soul" that belongs to all of us of the terrestrial biota.

(So much for the vain artist; I understand that there are also vain scientists.)

COOPERATIVE ALLIES

In all sincerity, the scientist should admit that his work for a logical, scientific civilization, with its conveniences and its easing of the laborious struggle for shelter and daily bread, is aimed at providing the time and knowledge necessary for the enjoyment of the arts and crafts, for the creation and enjoyment of the colors, aromas, and nuances of the uppermost fringes of human evolution. The swine and fowls strive for food and shelter; the bees and ants exploit the social advantages of food conservation, orderly government, and the hygienic care of offspring. But apparently it is man alone who struggles, in spite of individual greed and obstructing egocentrisms, to build through the sciences a physical and social environment which will permit a large-scale elaboration of his ganglia and nerve endings—which will permit, that is, the maintenance and elaboration of the Humanistic Tradition.

It is of this ganglionic elaboration that I would speak in concluding my brief essay into compromise. The sciences and the Humanistic Tradition are not too far apart—if we lop off or ignore at one end the unthinking mechanists, at the other end the soft-handed dilettanti. If our humanists could find time and inclination to look into the natural sciences with sympathy, rather than with the too-frequent defense mechanism of disdain, I believe they would find the field alive with hormones for revitalizing the Humanistic Tradition. They should not be dismayed by the complications and difficulties of technology, of chemistry, electronics, and mathematics. They should modestly admit their intellectual limitations. True scientists, freely agnostic, early abandon the pose of near-omniscience. For the scientist in one field is mystified by those in other fields—sometimes by colleagues in his own field, or a week later mystified even by himself!

A sympathetic approach by the non-scientist toward the contents and goals of the sciences should pay well in the coin of philosophical comprehension, as well as in artistic raw material. If our introspective artist, bent on self-expression, would reorient himself in the content of present human knowledge and contemplate deeply, not superficially, the vibrant oscillations in the electron tubes, the poetic geometries of protein structure, the sculpture of a beetle's back, and the majesty of the cosmic processes that play with bursting stars, with radiation that penetrates bone and iron, with time scales that tempt the unwary to speculate on Creation—if he learned to appreciate all this, our artist would then find that modern science is his cooperative ally, not his heartless opponent.

11

Must We Climb Steeples?

When confronted with the question, What can scholarship do in a world crisis? I am inclined to say that it is helpless when crises are sharp and immediate. But if the pangs that contort the civilization are moderately prolonged, with the decisive days far ahead, then I begin to murmur about education and its reputedly salutary effects. So far, I must admit, education as a therapy has not kept us in sufficiently good social health to withstand crucial strains and tensions. Perhaps education itself needs therapeutic attention.

Proceeding toward a diagnosis, and operating as an advocate of action rather than as an addict of philosophical analysis, I should like to present here a modest program as a preface to some bigger and better overall plan for using the trained mind effectively in human crises.

Many practical prescriptions for scholarship in action, in humble and effective action for the good of all men, could be written. Such proposals could also be "action-prescriptions" for non-scholars. And it is the unschooled, rather than the learned, who are likely to welcome the social and political contribution of the scholar-citizen. For his fellow scholars are likely to fret about proprieties. The arched eyebrow of the arch-scholar is often an obstacle to practical social service. Iron curtains with only small peepholes surround many of our specialists—curtains which are opaque both inward and outward. Through such curtains intercourse with the unschooled is difficult, as is also intercourse with scholars of other fields.

Is the following illustration an irrelevant interruption? My own studies and fragmentary knowledge deal with cosmogony; that is, with the eternities and infinities, with the origins and destinies, with the relation of man to his majestic universe. Sounds a bit like natural piety. Sounds as if I could be useful theologically. And I have been invited to speak in Cooper Union, in the New York Town Hall forum, in Madison Square Garden, but never, never, in St. John the Divine or any other cathedral, and with two notable exceptions, not in any divinity school where the shepherds of men's souls are trained and conditioned. Is there something tragically significant in this divine retreat from knowledge? Is there doubt about the ability of souls to face the facts about the stars?

These remarks on social activities for scholars are a proper introduction to the question raised in this chapter: Must we climb steeples? In other words, how far should we permit ourselves to go in specialism? Intellectual isolation may be an attempt to escape responsibility.

The habit of steeple-climbing has, alas, helped to divert

us from our civic duties. The intellectual, in spite of his specialization, should he not be a soldier in the army that makes
democracy and Christian ethics work? Should he not serve
with the glazier, the plumber, the brewer, the pilot, and other
specialists?

I have felt extremely frustrated every time I have climbed
a steeple. I could not branch out. I was unable to increase
appreciably the height of the steeple and go on upward.
There was no place to go but down, unless, like the flagpole
sitter, I chose to remain perched, an inert human blob at the
pinnacle—exposed, meanly vain, triumphantly silly.

I now propose a deliberate opposition to steepling. Let
me take a tilt at one or two steeples and see if I get unhorsed,
or if I cause them to totter a bit.

SHOULD WE ABANDON EDUCATION?

During the past 20 years, more than 200 thoughtful Americans have publicly insisted that serious defects exist in our
system of higher education. Dozens have written books which
in themselves amply demonstrated the defects. Our teachers,
it is insisted, are improperly trained; the curriculum is a
mess; the students are allergic to study; the ideals are perverted; the future is black.

No one proposes the obvious alternative of giving up education altogether and restoring the happiness that frequently goes with total ignorance; no one advocates that we
diminish the worry that accompanies wisdom. Such ad-
vocacy is certainly a temptation. If I had not learned to read
and write, I should have been spared much weary labor,
much distressing worry; and you also would have been
spared your current distress. You would have been spared

my panacea, which, like the other hundreds in recent years, is aimed at the salvage of our allegedly decadent educational system.

Not so long ago, in terms of cosmic time-scales, higher education was practiced for the advantage of the clergy. It would perhaps enrich sermons; it was indeed a desperate device to diminish deadly dullness. History records that education did not help much. But the social prestige of book-learning was useful. Prestige accrued not only to preachers but also to the laymen who sought advanced education in the restricted curriculums of those primitive days. The clergy and laymen both enjoyed practical gain through education, an advantage over other men and other beasts, although such acquired knowledge then, as now, availed little against time, death, and the galaxies.

While the curriculums of the institutions of higher learning have swung back and forth from static to fluid, from general education to high specialization for a practical life, the social prestige of higher education has continued to veneer the participants and their institutions. Eventually many began to see that the veneer is essentially all there is to the higher educational structure. The termites of sports and social activities have gnawed away the body of the building. Education has become largely a superficial device for concealing the ignorance within. But, I ask, is not veneer better than nothing? With the modern techniques, they make excellent veneer these days.

As I say, the professional educators have devoted much time since the beginning of the century to writing books at each other about curricular and educational policies at the college level. Some good has undoubtedly come therefrom.

Experiments are being tried here and there. The current trend is to curb the presumed evils of specialization in our institutions of mass education through the introduction, especially in the early years of college, of "general education courses." The Chicago system, the Columbia system, the Colgate system (not to get out of the C's) have drawn some commendation and much criticism. The criticism has come especially from those educators who have not yet produced a comparable cure for the presumed evils, or from those who are already riding the pendulum back to (as they put it) "sound training in chosen special fields and consequent escape from scattered dilettantism." (Aren't words wonderful?)

My limited observations and experience have been mostly with students who are candidates for the master's or doctor's degree in astronomy. They happen to be not as distressing and distressed as students are likely to be in many other fields, because the undergraduate offerings in astronomy in American colleges are so few that the student in search of credits cannot restrict himself closely to the constellations and to the narrow confines of celestial activity. Because of the thinness of the undergraduate offerings in astronomy, he has generally, in spite of himself, been somewhat exposed to languages and the social sciences, to other physical sciences and the arts.

Of course, we must not think only of the higher education that leads to professionalism. A would-be professional scholar, half-educated under our prevailing system, usually has many years available after the doctorate in which to carry out corrective measures. Eventually he can, if he will, educate himself broadly.

THE PLIGHT OF THE CONCENTREE

But the non-professional, who stops formal education abruptly with his bachelor's degree and his athletic letters, must live out a long life intellectually on the nutrition provided by his four (or more) years of undergraduate experience. Is a physics major, for instance, ready for the lifetime pose of being an educated man? Or is the botany or history major fully prepared by his education to honor his teachers and his college? Or have they all merely climbed small, tapering steeples with no place to go afterward but down?

The one who concentrated on botany, for instance, cannot talk intellectually any more, he says, with those benighted colleagues who concentrated on mathematics, or with those who got their diploma credit in finance. The more advanced the botany major becomes, the narrower his steeple, the smaller his discussion group, the fewer his appreciators. Elementary biology, he found, was pretty widely interesting; it could provide communal conversation and even cooperative or solitary thinking; the second course, economic botany, still provides two or three thought-provoking arguments with, shall we say, engineers; but the ability to interest engineers disappears when cryptogams enter the picture. And all his classmates pass on the other side of the street with averted faces when the botany major, in his senior year, is filled up with Pteridophyta. The botanical steeplejack has isolated himself, and since he does not go on to professionalism, he naturally feels lonely and frustrated and hopes to heaven that the vaunted mental training he is alleged to have received will somehow help him when and if thinking is later required.

Once he is out of college, our botanical major is so baffled by his steeple isolation that he crawls down to the roof level, where he was at the end of high school; there he talks baseball, price levels, crops, and politics. He has had, perhaps, a healthy four years, but he confesses to the inquiring alumni secretary that he really got nothing out of college except good times and the chance to meet some swell guys in the fraternity and the gym. "Why don't they train people," he complains, "train them in some useful way? Or why don't they educate them broadly?" Or this or that?

There is no answer to those who aspire highly and lazily, and then uncover sadly their own limitations. And my heart is touched by those blobs perched wonderingly and uselessly on the steeples. My therapy would be to eliminate steeples from the undergraduate curriculum, permitting such structures to be erected or climbed only by experienced students who are launching out on professional careers.

The epidemic of general-education courses arises from recognition of the need for foundation education. Since this is a free country, where laymen can criticize the professionally élite, I question the efficacy and adequacy of the movement. It falls short in coverage, in both space and time. The general-education courses usual provide simply a little heavier foundation for small steeples, built and climbed by amateur craftsmen in junior and senior years. Occasionally, to be sure, an amateur's steeple stands, even grows, in alumni years; we are proud of this, and we tend to overpublicize it, forgetting the great majority whose parents pay for a fruitless gesture.

Stretching the architectural analogy, let us question whether the vertical structure is sound in a burgeoning world society. A structure composed only of columns has basic instability. An occasional crosstie helps, but it does not cure the defect in design. Why not introduce, deliberately, more horizontal members? Why not devote the whole of the four-year liberal arts college to horizontal structures which will serve as a capping for the secondary education and at the same time provide an exceedingly firm flooring for the erection of vertical members in the graduate school and later?

Reading, writing, and arithmetic are foundations built in the primary schools. The secondary schools provide science (natural and social). These are foundations for the students who go further, and they give intellectual experience and practical equipment to those who do not.

Now here is where you will not follow me or bear with me, for various reasons, especially if you are a professional college teacher. For I suggest that physics, government, economics, chemistry, biology, languages, and the other usual discrete subjects be not taught as such in college. As subjects they are proper for the secondary-school student, who is building tools for action; and then again, with a different intensity and content, they are proper for the narrow steeple-climbing specialist in the postgraduate years, although, even there, his success often depends largely on the horizontal tie-ups he makes with neighboring specialties. My proposal, or rather exploratory question, is: Should not all education-defeating vertical columns be eliminated from the college?

We have in America something more than two million undergraduate college students. Only a small fraction will go on to higher general education. Therefore what college does for those millions is rather important. They will get no more formal training, and they forget fast.

In college the undergraduates have been living integrated

lives, not as specialists. As alumni they will continue to live "across the disciplines." Most of them will not live as students of French Literature, or as medieval historians, or as biologists. They will be community citizens, mainly engaged in private enterprise of one sort or another. The ex-student will daily experience tensions which his education might alleviate if it did not suffer so much from the handicap of being columnarly specialized and not broadly comprehending.

THE PLATEAU CURRICULUM

What would take the place of the usual courses if we laid out a "plateau" curriculum constructed across the usual vertical disciplines? That should be a question for the professional educator. He might find a partial answer in the sample courses I am about to recommend, which certainly tend to illustrate the unity of knowledge and the attraction, if not the practicality, of the integrative approach. The courses I suggest might be inherently difficult to present and also hard to study and absorb, but skillful instructors could alleviate the pain through careful organization. There need be no fear of superficiality unless the instructors are superficial; the subjects are deep enough.

Here are some proposed across-disciplines courses, with the fields that each would include:

Course 1. *Societies*——At first blush, one might think that this most important subject for our struggling civilization would fall wholly in the field of social relations, or perhaps the field of cultural anthropology, or both. But further examination shows that the course should also draw heavily from the social insects, from political science, philosophy, demography, entomology, engineering, psychology, ethics, psychiatry, and other areas. It is a great subject, worthy of two or three course-years of undergraduate study. It should be oriented three ways—toward the past, the wide present, and the future.

Course 2. *Growth and Decay*——The importance of this subject would be perverted and largely concealed by any attack through only one discipline. Materials for its exploitation and presentation should come from the physical and social sciences and from the humanities as well as from biology, for growth and decay operate on galaxies, interstellar dust, and comets; on crystals, ideas, and biological individuals; on societies and social movements. The subject is wider than evolution. It embraces philosophy, chemistry, cosomogony, geology, literature, all aspects of biology, statistics, calculus, and history.

Course 3. *Communications*——A basic discipline in the lives of individuals, this course would draw from folkways, linguistics in many phases, biology, electronics, psychology, music, mechanical engineering, journalism, navigation, and ionospherics. An elementary phase of Course 1 would be an obvious prerequisite.

Course 4. *The Past*——This would present the history of the universe and mankind as deduced from geology, cosmogony, paleontology, anthropology, comparative neurology, political history, and so on. Here, wide integration is the essential key.

Course 5. *Religion*——A study of the contributions to religious belief from human psychology, history, social anthropology, literature, cosmogony, government, military strategy, and, of course, philosophy.

In addition to the foregoing, I suggest a group of courses which might be called "chronological analyses." Already, under titles such as "civilizations" or "this-or-that century's thought," our college curricula have widened the concept of history; it has been found profitable—a tempting gambit. I would go farther and wider. An example follows:

Course 6. *The Eighteenth Century*——Here would be included the history and interpretation of the creations and contributions of scholars, scientists, artists, merchants, and social and religious leaders, as well as the conventional recording of political and military developments. Professional historians of politics and of international political and military maneuvers probably should have little to do with this presentation and interpretation of the eighteenth century as a segment of the current world civilization. The historians appear to be badly be-steepled. When we interpret past ages, we should remember continuously the works of contributors such as Shakespeare, Kant, Laplace, Verdi, and Pavlov, and should minimize the doings of the prime ministers and military strategists.

Similarly, there could be across-the-board courses for other convenient time segments, in each of which routine history would be enriched, but perhaps almost submerged, by the contemporary contributions from other fields. For instance, the Atomic Age, beginning about 1897, should not be treated by a nuclear physicist alone, or a sociologist, or an economist. The atoms have invaded literature; they have transformed cosmogony; they have created new mathematics.

One who thus learns of segments of civilization across the fields of arts and sciences may easily live his own segment in a broader way. The most remarkable of the chronological courses could be "The Future" or "Twentieth Century, Second Half." It would involve Utopias (new and old), social threats like atomic war, world-population planning, T.V.A.-ing the planet, and dreams. In all probability it would be too hot to handle in the sobriety of the academic groves.

There are, in addition to those just named, several important multi-disciplined fields suitable for a college curriculum: for example, transportation, the mind, machines, dwellings, substances, civilizations, the Renaissance, and the gaseous envelope. All are thought-provoking. All can be easily programmed. Exploratory educators could find diversion and perhaps considerable profit in outlining the contents of these and the foregoing courses.

In a sense, I am simply proposing education by way of major *general* problems rather than by studies in traditional specialties—problems rather than subjects, if one defines those concepts suitably.

To round out my comments on the horizontal curriculum, I should admit, of course, that some of the trade schools —for engineering, agriculture, dentistry, and the like—must go on non-educating students and training them excellently for early specialization in the respective crafts and trades. The pre-medical requirements, for example, would demand of some students certain vertical components in the otherwise horizontal schedule (unless the specialized professional training in medicine be prolonged still further toward middle life).

My concluding comment on this particular exploration by a skeptical steeplejack is that we should recognize the fact that the atomic age has opened a new world for educators. We should continue to worry about stabilities and equilibria,

and continue to ask if it is an intelligent policy to promote
intellectual isolationism through the early climbing of poorly
grounded steeples.

THE BOREDOM OF SCIENTIFIC
MEETINGS

I took higher education and its steeples for my first tilt.
Let us now take on scientific societies, but without going
into laborious detail. At the large scientific conventions, and
in the ordinary meetings of most of the technical scientific
societies, the specialized steeplejacks often exhibit themselves to no good end.

The ordinary "meeting for papers" of the technical scientific societies is really droll in its toleration of steepling. This
technical specializing probably holds to a lesser degree in
meetings of philosophers; probably much less among historians, educators, and others who generally keep away
from mathematics and the technologies. I have sat through
dozens of scientific meetings where I understood less than
half of what was going on. I was lost, from the beginning to
the too-distant end. Often it was not important that I did
not understand. The greater part of the audience was in my
condition, or even worse off. It was only vaguely interested in
the parade of technical minutiae or complicated reasoning.
But still the listeners sat, lost in day dreaming, or just sitting,
or frequently frankly sleeping.

Why do scientists, otherwise intelligent, endure these
specialized papers that are imposed on 50 to 500 people,
when only two or three colleagues of the speaker are really
interested and profiting? The putative listeners' endurance
is, I suppose, in part a gesture of timid good manners; in

part a bluff; in part a heroic expression of personal good will toward the performer. But what a waste! If all those who do not really understand or do not care to hear the indifferent presentation of some technical work would only walk out of the scientific meetings, it would result in immediate reform, possibly revolution! The synthetic dullness of most meetings drives many a self-respecting man into seclusion at times of meetings and keeps him out of contact with his fellow workers. He seeks and uses shallow excuses for his absence.

There are remedies. One is simply to omit most of the papers. Another remedy, often applied, is to discourage narrowly technical papers and make up a program emphasizing in their stead symposiums and cross-field conferences. Also, occasionally a give-and-take round table is put on to alleviate the pains of a meeting. As we get braver, ruder, and more aware of the disadvantage of steepling in public, the wasteful and rather stupid technical exhibitions will lose appeal to the exhibitor as well as to the audience.

I should not want to be misunderstood about concentrated specialization. I am all for it, and definitely averse to popularization in technical company. But since our brains are limited and rather weary, let us practice mental economy and, as scholars, go running up our chosen steeples *only* when occasion really demands it.

The possibility of getting out of our narrow specialties when working for worldwide peace and on other social problems leads me to urge as a concluding thought that scholarship can best contribute to the amelioration of international tensions by keeping out of ivory steeples and integrating its operations over the horizontal surfaces where diplomats and common men live and work and misbehave.

12

The Cultivation of
Learning for Its Own Sake

In the dawn of terrestrial life, learning for its own sake was cultivated along the paleozoic shores. The early animal adventurer clumsily ascended the mysterious strand, impelled by curiosity. It would have been easier for him to conform with the Higher Gracefulness, swimming cleverly with the stream, or perishing naturally as the food of some Greater Necessity. But out of the slimy water-edge came this ancient investigator. I visualize him: in the early light he crawls to the top of some trivial pinnacle, cranes his neck, pricks up his still incipient ears, gazes around at land and sea, stares stupidly at the stars with unpracticed eyes, and inquires: "How come?"

He was inspired with primitive wonderment, this early

156

explorer. He had become cognotropic—turned, that is, toward knowledge for its own sake. This new and growing tendency, or tropism, which was destined to lead haltingly to the evolution of the highest animals, was at first faint and useless compared with other tropisms—with the geotropic, hydrotropic, phototropic responses that guided life in those early days and made deliberate thinking unnecessary.

But weak though it may have been, that Paleozoic feeling of curiosity was of the same sort of impelling urge to explore the shores as I myself now represent. He was a Silurian scientist, and I am neo-Pleistocene. The only serious difference between us that I can see is that my early colleague did not have to write up his squeaks of wonderment for the Harvard Alumni Bulletin.

My confreres of the Silurian Period possessed and transmitted only a lower form of cognotropism. (Since the word "cognotropism" may be overlooked by your dictionary, I should perhaps sacrifice the good polysyllable and resort to the simplification: "innate urge to know.") This urge, this research spirit of the more up-and-coming animals of the Paleozoic, incited them to an indulgence in what I would call "random curiosity," in distinction from the Harvard program of "directed inquisitiveness."

CURIOSITY IS CONGENITAL

Among us higher primates, the urge to know is of course inevitably transmitted by the germ plasm, both in quantity and in intensity. Some degree of native inquisitiveness is always manifest. We need not incite the baby to curiosity. He early crawls out of the stream of living comfortably and seeks contact with bitter experience. Curiosity of a sort is passed along like the other instincts. Many important disciplines do not need educators. The hungry wolf needs no dietetic advice. The young moth or butterfly, intent on progeny, never depends on the pedagogues. Her mother has told her nothing. She has read no confession magazines. Nevertheless, caterpillars eventuate.

The congenital urge to know and explore can be turned to the profit of social organization. But too often we harness native curiosity and drive it, sometimes unhappily, along the dusty roads of traditional schooling. Its fresh, sharp edge is often dulled thereby, but, in recompense, a higher goal is ultimately reached through contact with systematic procedures.

Beside the streams of organized learning, two types of inquisitiveness become apparent. Generally we say simply: "I want to know because it will get me a license to practice medicine, or to extract a tooth so that I can extract a fee with which to extract meat and drink from the vendors thereof, so that I can then have strength and courage to extract more teeth for more coins for more food for more strength for more. . . ." There appears to be a whirlpool in the stream, and one wonders which way is forward. Is the goal the extracting of ever larger dollars or the pulling of ever better teeth?

But some may say: "I want to know because—well, because I was just wondering."

Now both of these types of curiosity—cash-and-carry and wonderment—are sociologically transmitted. They are inevitable in our sons as they were in us. We are likely to praise the first type as ambition, and deplore the second as idle curiosity and dreaming. It is this "just wondering," however, that has produced the higher man, transformed the art of living, built up philosophies, elevated the physically low human to a place at the high table with the gods. But I should not become breathless in my praise of curiosity. It has its limitations. It leads frequently to catastrophe. There is much stumbling as we grope upward. If we depended wholly on the payoff of "random curiosity," we would remain intellectually with the inquisitive magpie and the prying cat.

Directed inquiry seems to be more effective than random research, although throughout the land we still have individuals who ask for complete and random freedom in research activities—freedom in speech, also in writing, in thinking, in all things freedom. This unbridled and presumably undirected curiosity frequently brings rich reward, but there were rewards more often in Silurian times than now. In satisfying our present curiosities we must depend much on machinery for experimenting, and on libraries for orientation. Purposeful guiding is therefore needed, and for directed inquisitiveness we need historical background. This tool, History, is the supreme instrument of man aspiring to material and spiritual maturity. By history, of course, I do not mean the chronicles of the wars and greeds of the higher primates. My "history" includes the orally transmitted wisdom of ancient shepherds, and the recording of human enterprises on cavern walls, on skins, and eventually on rags and paper pulp. My history includes the new edition of *Guido della Colonne,* and the measurements of Arcturian wavelengths as reported in the current *Zeitschrift für Astrophysik.* It is history in this sense that makes our cultivation of knowledge for its own sake effective, and at the same time diminishes the joy and usefulness of that random curiosity which gave so much pleasure to the ancient grasshopper and to our own predecessors.

We do get pleasure in our directed curiosity, but it is now a somewhat grim and determined joy. Our assaults on the unknown are deliberate. Research is essentially a business. It is, to be sure, a high endeavor, protected and subsidized because in recent times society has recognized that the acquisition of new knowledge is the responsibility of the human race. It is an opportunity as well as a responsibility. No other terrestrial plant or animal is so well endowed that it can fruitfully aspire to cosmic comprehension. No other civilization that our species managed to build up was so well equipped as is the present one, with legible records and with natural and artificial tools, equipped to give the human cortex its chance to advance—its opportunity to understand man and the universe, to unravel the many knots along the road and perhaps even the master knot of human fate.

It is the profession of many of us to add to the world's store of knowledge. We also train others in this business of being creative scholars. When large and laborious projects are under way, we employ some of the techniques of the factory. For example, we study galaxies at the Harvard Observatory in a large endeavor to survey the Metagalaxy to a depth of a hundred million light years. Galaxy hunting and recording is and must be an efficiently operated business. No one has ever explored in this manner before, and with as powerful equipment as we now have available. A million galaxies will be found (our sampling indicates), and their types, magnitudes, dimensions, and positions determined. All is done in the interest of knowing more of the structure of the world, knowing more of its contents and its principles, the epochal dates in its development, and the peculiar behavior of space, time, matter, and natural law, not only during this moment of terrestrial life, but also at the beginning of space-time, and at the ultimate boundaries.

GIRL-HOURS AND GALAXIES

Extensive labor and organization are required for the galaxy survey. It is not a task for a dreamy mind, or for feckless philosophy. A research bureau is indispensable. The advance is in terms of astrophotographic plates and girl-hours. Together they lead us to the secrets of the universe. And by girl-hours and secrets I do not mean the romantic concepts that perhaps flit through your mind—"The Hours I Spend with Thee, Dear Heart"—no, none of that sort of nonsense. I mean by girl-hours certain cold-blooded, unromantic units of labor, analogous to horsepower and kilowatts. (We have tried boy-hour units also, but, at least in the Observatory, they prove to be dumber and sloppier units.)

The discovery of a basically important metagalactic density gradient—a result which immediately affects, perhaps profoundly, our contemplations in relativistic cosmogony—cost Harvard University 2.6 kilogirl-hours, in addition to an even dozen of directorial headaches. It was, in a sense, a business proposition, and not inexpensive. The discovery and measurement of galaxies is now costing us about $52 a hundred, but with increasing managerial skill we are hoping to bring this down, for the next hundred thousand objects, to $48 a hundred. A new variable star, raw but recorded, costs about $9, and three times that amount when fully observed and published.

Theories, of course, are less easily budgeted; the overhead is high, and they are perishable. Observational facts, however, and I say this in all seriousness, whether they concern the counts of remote stars, the speeds of neutrons, the correctness of editions of Virgil—good observations keep well, change styles slowly, and for the elevation of this groping race of primates they are tremendously sound investments. The observations are essential, moreover, if we are to be comfortable in our thoughts and dreams. The proper cultivation of learning, whether for its own sake or for your sake, requires the intelligent use of our sense organs in the accumulation of significant facts, followed by a gentle play of the imagination—all of these operations inspired by the primal curiosity.

The urge to know has evolved from an instinct into a profession. Because of its necessary relation to the expensive apparatus of experiment and to the accumulation of historical records in libraries and museums, the systematic explorations are necessarily centralized where learned men are together— that is, in colleges, universities, and endowed research institutions. There the exploration of past, present, and future must be maintained if the ultimate direction of our civilization is to be up and outward with the expanding universe.

An obvious danger threatens this upward and outward progress. It lies in the increasing tendency to move toward the satisfaction of a modified curiosity that has as its goal not satisfaction of wonderment but achievement of some specific end, often a political or economic end. Unless we can serve the desire to find out, unencumbered by a concern for particular political results, the urge to know will be stifled by utility. We shall find ourselves not exploring on the shores but floundering in the stagnant waters of an arrested intellectual development.

The cause of this danger is a distorted concept of the

powers and the responsibility of the human mind. It would avail little if evolving man were merely to substitute a complicated animality in the place of his primitive junglism. It would avail still less if he were to waste his enormous powers of thought and action on a way of living that could be achieved only by force, in one form or another. Creative curiosity would perish, as all characteristics perish when they have no survival value. And with it would be destroyed all claims of mankind for a place at the high table, all hope for a still higher form of evolution, or for any claim to real eminence in the earth's animal kingdom.

Fortunately, however, we widely realize that, notwithstanding the amenities of life provided by current civilization, our really serious claim to superiority lies primarily in that high faculty that permits us to use our cerebral equipment to seek out knowledge for its own sake and for the sake of the seeking—to pursue the program of "just wondering."

13

The Coming World State

Before inquiring about the immediate future for intellectuals—for the scientist, artist, professional, and white-collar worker generally—I should like to make two observations, the first rather superficial, the second deep and perhaps frightening.

The first is that there are many people who haven't white collars but do have souls. They have feelings, too, for beauty and for the wonders of art and nature. And conversely, the white-collar professionals, the artists, and the scientists have among them many an ignorant boor. Thinking is done not with white collars but with gray matter.

The second point: A world-state is in prospect for the very near future. (This may not terrify you; it does not me.) World-state means the unitary organization of terrestrial mankind. I am, of course, a little touched with the language of the stars when I use the phrase "very near future" as the time for the coming world unity; I mean "cosmically" soon —before the planet Pluto, for instance, has completed its present circuit around the sun, in about 250 of our years. In its current circuit, Pluto, which has already made about ten million round trips, will be able to witness, if interested, our social evolution from an Earth of many squabbling nations to an Earth with its people all in one reasonably peaceful organization.

THE VISIONS OF PLUTO

I should like at this point to stress again something that many writers have emphasized: namely, that the nations of the earth have been brought into close contact, physically and mentally, by speedboat, airplane, radio, atomic engines, and moving pictures. We can now readily distribute all over the planet the same diseases and the same dopes. The planet is too small for separationism. But how soon can we distribute common sense and common hopes?

The quality and degree of the internationalism of the coming world-state should be explored. A world-wide economic association encompassing all states that do business with one another seems so ultimately inevitable that one wonders why we are trying futile half-way substitutes. Also, the unified political organization that will encompass all the present nations, supernations, and subnations appears likely to develop rapidly, notwithstanding some stubborn and probably bloody resistance. The unit nation will emerge long before Pluto returns to Aries. That is my prediction. Some would probably prefer to predict that the political unity will be obtained and stabilized before the end of the present century; others may hold out for a thousand years of blood and political individualism. But I sincerely believe we would all agree, if put to it, that eventually either we sink to savagery or rise to a world unity, however drab this last prospect may appear.

The all-inclusive business-and-political systems of the future will involve commerce (economics) and the protection and regulation of commerce (government); and as these systems become established, the truly international man will emerge.

THE CONSERVATION OF LOCAL CULTURE

International we shall become in business and politics, but is a worldwide common culture a necessity and an inevitability of the new order? I believe not. I hope not. A political supranation and universal economic agreements need not necessarily lead to a sterile uniformity in the cultural world. Local languages will give way very slowly, and many local customs will persist because they are linked with local geography. The hills, valleys, mountains, seashores, and various belts of latitude will long remain much as now, notwithstanding the ingenuity and deviltry of man. And the climates, soils, waters, and scenery of the various localities can have a persisting effect on the folkways of whatever inhabitants choose to remain, or are permitted to remain, in such relatively specialized domains.

That cultures (whether of man, plant, or animal) resist change, and that localized distinctiveness can be preserved, is demonstrated for man in all the large countries of the world by the persisting social differences between contiguous groups. And only if the world maintains the human cultural varieties, as endemic cultures, will it provide enough diversity and natural opportunities for mankind's evolution. I mean here evolution in taste and art, as well as growth in industry and natural science.

Admitting that the peaceful success of international society seems to make necessary among the other requirements a good American social system, I turn with timidity to practical problems of the day. Certainly I do not know enough to make prophecies. No crystal-gazing, or horoscopy, or even experience and wisdom, can foretell the future that may develop out of the tensions of cold wars and nervous peace in this atomic era. It will be best to prophesy nothing, but rather to present briefly a miscellany of hopes.

One preliminary fervent hope is that we shall continue to realize that our own educational system, especially in the sciences, is as yet so far from being streamlined to the times that we should not consider our policies worthy of being foisted on other nations. The scientific talent upon which our advance and security in the future may largely depend will be, I hope, methodically hunted out and developed. We shall have our hands so full in finding and training our own future leaders and analysts that there is little point in our offering unwanted socio-economic advice abroad. We may instruct others better through our performance than by our words.

Some of us have cheerful hopes for the methodical encouragement of craftmanship in country, town, and city. Already much is done, and it has been tremendously worthwhile. In one small field where I am acquainted, amateur telescope making, we have not only created an art and hobby for thousands of people in America, but created a profession for many. With much help from its amateur telescope-makers, America has captured the lead in optical work of many sorts. The further practical development of craftsmen in pottery, glass, paint, woodwork, the metals, and electronics is a problem that requires only inspiration and organization; America is rich in both.

My major hope, in this brief confession of optimism, is that the local American community will grow in cultural self-sufficiency. We are quite willing to give over to international organization the responsibility for the larger political and economic managements, if such delegation means peace, efficiency, and progress. But let us work toward both a brave and a colorful new world through the maintenance of our local customs and cultures.

There are doubtless many ways of maintaining the dignity of the individual in this earthly colony of more than three billion fairly similar people. As one contribution to the desired cultural heterogeneity of mankind, the small community, we hope, will continue to live and think and play by *itself*. It is high time that we got started on a program of the deliberate cultivation of community life. For we must admit that much of our thinking and feeling has now been delegated to others through the dominance of chain newspapers, broadcasting syndicates, and movie theaters. It is alarming to realize how many of us hear the same news commentators, the same comedians and music analyzers; and to realize how many of us read the same "comic" strips, eat the same kinds of food, announce the same profound observations on forthcoming events. Unconsciously, we have delegated our thinking, our feeling, much of our tasting, and even the intonation of our trite comments to a few score men and women who have gained access to our broadcasting studios, our newspapers, and our food-jobbers.

All of this has gone so far that escape from uniformity seems impossible. Originality in thought and expression have been sold down the river for the joy of hearing a hot gag.

We cannot retrace and start over, and most of us would not want to—we are mentally lazy, and too willing to follow leaders. But can we not counteract a little the deadening effect of this national centralized domination, by emphasizing the activities of localized natural communities? Cannot scientists, and professional people generally, take over constructive leadership in the intellectual and artistic phases of human growth and destiny?

CAN DIVERSE CULTURES SURVIVE?

I can state a little more clearly what I recommend by citing a few examples:

1. Much of the work of the thousands of science clubs, in the schools and among adults, deals with the biology, topography, industry, and archaeology of the local region. Such interests foster the pride of the local populace. A particular county or valley may well take pride, for instance, in gaining an excellent knowledge of its own plant life, relating it to the flora of larger regions, and applying the knowledge to the community's horticultural problems.

2. The rise of small symphony orchestras and choruses, and the growth of amateur musical performance, are signs that we can develop genuine loyalties to the ambitious homefolks, and really enjoy their work, notwithstanding the canned perfection that could be ours by the turning of a radio dial. Support of these musical movements, especially

when they can be related to the folksongs and folklore of the community, is a responsibility for all of us who recognize the dullness of perfection, the importance of the independent life of the community, and the heightened likelihood of the evolution of taste and intelligence if homogeneity is opposed.

3. On a somewhat higher level of accomplishment, perhaps possible only in the smaller cities, is the local scientific research institution. Such communities have long had art museums, sometimes natural history museums, and frequently important musical organizations. The community has stood back of such enterprises as a civic responsibility, and the greater the local pride, the better these community institutions have become. I have been from its founding associated with such a community organization in the field of experimental biology;* I can testify to the appeal of this pioneer enterprise, and testify also to its merit locally and nationally.

In cities or towns where there are active research laboratories and libraries connected with colleges, there is less need for additional community research centers. But there are many cities, with populations between 50,000 and 500,000, where as yet there is no active public interest in the discovery of new truth and the creation of new knowledge. In some of these places there are important hospitals, or extensive engineering industries, both of which could supply a personnel interested in the direct advance of knowledge, pure or applied. The research programs of such a community foundation might focus on investigations of some particular interest to the region; or better yet, they might be unrelated to the

---

* The Worcester Foundation for Experimental Biology.

community's immediate interest but be recognized as important to mankind generally. The local research foundation would stand, therefore, as the community's own responsibility for the advancement of civilization. Such enterprises as the biological foundation I am associated with require competent personnel and financial support; that is also true of the symphony orchestras and the art museums.

I conclude by repeating that the responsibilities and opportunities for professional men and women, for scientists and artists of all kinds, include a social duty on a high level. We should not leave to practical politicians, or to uniformity-producing centralized broadcasters, the shaping of the future, either for the individual or for natural communities.

14

Is Mankind Entering the Psychozoic Kingdom?

The times are clearly out of joint, and it is time to do something about them. Revised educational plans such as proposed above are not enough. Deep meditation, fresh contemplation, a pondering of the imponderables are fine qualities that we should strive to establish—that is, if we would live constructively in the evolving Psychozoic Era. We should contemplate fresh horizons. But this decision leads me to inquire: What is wrong with the old horizons? Certainly they are not outgrown.

In these days of fast and routine living we rarely budget time for contemplating horizons and goals. The customary patterns of routine behavior and of popular parroting suit us pretty well—most of us. We are resigned, apparently, to what is; the grooves of the pattern and the bromides of the parrot are comfortable. Emphasis on the near and the immediate reduces our worry about what lies far ahead in time, and far away in space. Moreover, those horizons, when we do timidly look at them, appear to be infected with nightmares and inhabited by misanthropic dragons. We relish neither.

Doubtless the horizons of the past decade or two could now be profitably readjusted. Adjusted with profit, that is, if we who seek them for ourselves and for others would bring the evaluation of goals into keeping with our new understanding of man and the universe.

In the world of protoplasmic organisms man is an extraordinary construct. He is forever looking backward over his shoulder (history-minded), and sometimes timidly far forward (utopia-minded). We believe that he is unique in this respect. The tree and the flower do not bother much about the seeking of new horizons. Apparently the beast and the bug have presently no goals that differ from those of the Pliocene, two million years ago. They live a routine pattern; their programs are clear. Individual survival through self-defense, physical growth through the ingestion of familiar and habitual foods, propagation of offspring in the interest of survival of the family and species—these are the facts and acts in the life-grasping by the bees and flowers.

But man, while sharing with other organisms the same basic vital drives and goals, has got himself into a transcendency where survival is not necessarily a major inspiration. He seeks goals that involve more than his own fate. The enlarged frontal lobes of his brain have brought with them the concepts and practices of charity, altruism, and mutual respect—and also greed, mendacity, distrust, and similar less happy qualities. These are all human qualities, or at least they are more strongly manifest in man than in the less thoughtful and less scheming animals.

This mental complex, this forebrain of the most specialized primate, has so complicated his life that programs for living now appear to be essential. And the program-planning requires a philosophy of living and of life which we describe as an assembly of ideals. We might say with reason that programs of life, so defined, are indulged in deliberately by man but not by plants and the other animals. I do not feel too sure about this statement. Are we not rather hasty in asserting that the varied artifacts and ceremonies of animals, such as those of the social insects, are purely instinctive, no matter how complex and how peculiarly adapted they are to conditions of the moment? And are we not equally hasty in saying that men are thought-guided animals, in spite of the evidence that mostly we react rather than think?

Let us look further into the hypothesis that we alone make programs for living, and for working toward ethereal ideals. We shall not question the present physical dominance of man over other animals on this small planet in a run-of-the-mill solar system near the rim of a routine but oversize galaxy. There are now more than three billions of men, but all are included in one species. Notwithstanding some variety in skin color, stature, and clothing habits, man and the proverbial pea-in-the-pod follow a monotonous standard. *Homo* has two arms and two legs and one nose. Quite foolish of me to make such a statement? No! If some men had three legs or four arms or as many smellers as a butterfly, we could easily and reasonably fabricate a superior-inferior race hypothesis. The wasps, for instance, do have such a diversity of form and habits; there are hundreds of species, and by one criterion or another we might easily sort out "superior" species, which doubtless would have different "ideals" in their labor of horizon-seeking. But man has no such diversity.

The ecological horizons of the insects change slowly with the geological ages. Some minor adjustments they make promptly, however, as a result of man's economic interference. For example, his intercontinental commerce has brought to North America the Dutch elm disease and the Japanese beetle. These organisms, at their own level, now have new, or at least expanded, horizons. And, similarly, through his commerce and cultural growth man has greatly disturbed his own old environments, both material and spiritual. In consequence his physical and psychical horizons and programs are changing.

Now I see that I can answer my opening question: What is wrong with the old horizons? Nothing much. They were good in their day and for their clientele. The need for new horizons arises simply because the terrain has changed. The old horizons no longer fit. What were sometimes steep uphill climbs are now gentle downhill ski runs. What had appeared to our insufficiently trained minds to be conquered and occupied scientific territory has bristled up with doubts and mysteries and perhaps impossible barriers. The ingenuity of the rather ingenuous primate has re-ordered the terrain, set up new values, and brought to himself a questioning confusion.

THE VIRTUES OF THE HYMENOPTERA

Let us look toward some of these altered horizons and see if yesterday's ideals may still suffice. And on the way let us wonder if we can assuredly maintain ourselves above the animal level. The ants, bees, termites, and wasps are social groups of great antiquity that have developed many morphological specialties and social characteristics. Forty million years before man appeared, they had acquired successful social relationships in a variety of forms. Then, as now, they practiced the higher virtues and some of the most intricate technologies now known to man. Altruism, cooperation among individuals, and patriotism are natural to scores of different kinds of the hymenopterous insects. Some of them know and use community sanitation, air conditioning, anesthesia, birth control, fungus culture, and of course the making of wax, honey, and paper. They have long displayed numerous talents which man has only recently acquired.

These astonishing, well-tried social developments, which came into existence long before nature devised the higher primates out of a humbler past, should be kept in mind when we contemplate the possibilities of biological evolution on the other livable planets scattered throughout the cosmos. We must be ready to believe that such high developments have occurred in many of those worlds. They probably parallel the high biological adventures on this planet's surface, for we find the same chemistry in distant galaxies as in our own, the same responses to gravitation, the same relationships between matter, energy, space, and time. The operations of physics and chemistry are apparently the same everywhere. Therefore we should expect to find, wherever our telescopes lead us, the same sort of biochemical reactions whenever the physical conditions permit the existence of organisms. Whatever life exists elsewhere necessarily should be similar to the life here—similar in general pattern and quality. But elsewhere there may have been more time for some phases of biological evolution, or better topographic environments, or more propitious characteristics of stellar radiation or planetary stability, with the result that elsewhere life has been able to go higher, perhaps much higher, than anything we know.

In surveying new horizons, and in formulating programmatic ideals, we would do well to keep always in mind that this stellar universe includes a great many experiments in the higher biologies. Doubtless numerous domiciles of life have produced beings more sentient than we, beings more comprehending, more experiencing, and possibly, by their unimaginable standards, more divine than we. (You are of course at liberty to deny, as categorically as I affirm, the existence of these other-world carriers of "spirit," but why not face the evidence and think it through?)

It is not difficult to see how improvements on man could be made, however we define "improvements." For example, as remarked in an earlier chapter, man does not possess well-developed sense organs to tell him very fully what is what. We have no good physiological register of long electric waves and must resort to gadgetary feelers. We have no bodily organ for sensing directly the ultraviolet radiation, or the infrared. Some stars have enormous magnetic fields; ours has a relatively weak one. We have no recognizable magnetic sense organ; it may naturally be otherwise elsewhere.

As every anatomist knows, man is physically primitive in some respects, and in others rather dangerously specialized. His primitivism and his physiological oddities (brains, for example) may erase him suicidally from the earth. His clinging to the past keeps him most of the time at the animal level—food, fight, shelter, procreation. Unfortunately, his reaching for heaven and the stars may eventually disconnect him from his animal sources of physical and neurological strength.

READJUSTING GOALS

Apparently up to this point I am not very optimistic about *Homo*. But my doubts refer to the past and the present. What lies ahead is another judgment. With new horizons recognized, and ideals continually adjusted to the growth of man's knowledge, the man of the future can perhaps justify our inclination to glorify him as the central showpiece in a new biological kingdom.

Postponing a further interview with the stars, let us look around, far, wide, and back a billion years in earth history. We then recognize in the biological world two kingdoms—animal and vegetable. Are they the only organic kingdoms that could be produced on this planet? On remote and happier planets there may be life forms other than plant and animal—other major kingdoms of life.

But have we not, right here and now on Earth, the beginning of a third major category—the Psychozoic Kingdom? Now I know it is vanity, almost anthropocentrism, to sort out *Homo sapiens* and say that he differs so much from the chimpanzees, spiders, and oysters that he merits a kingdom of his own—differs so much that we can set up for him a separate set of natural laws, much as we can separate the rules for plants from the rules for animals. But vanity and hopeful wishing aside, the evidence is good that the forebrain—our large time-binding cortex—is something very remarkable in the animate world, and perhaps justifies the separate classification.

We cannot draw a sharp boundary between man and

his forebears. Certainly man developed from simpler, less thoughtful organic forms. The series is continuous from the lowest algae to the highest primates. I assume that the chimps, the termites, the orchids, the viruses and their advocates will not object if we claim only that we are now on the way to the establishment of a Psychozoic Kingdom where brain overshadows brawn and rationality overshadows natural instinct.

I have almost brought myself to the point of believing that man is important in the universe. But I want you to keep in mind that his psychozoic development, now blossoming among the higher primates on this planet, has probably long since been richly attained in some other inhabited worlds. At this point in our contemplations we begin to glimpse a cosmic goal for ourselves. Although we are out of touch (except in the imagination) with the high-life organisms elsewhere, we can compete with them, as the Eras roll along, in advancing the *third biological kingdom.* We see faintly a mystical light glimmering on a new horizon.

As the free-moving animals outdo the anchored, sunshine-sucking plants from which they sprang, so do we free-thinking humans outdo our ancestral animals, anchored to their instincts. To advance further toward ultimate goals, it is clear that our program-for-life should turn away more and more from the animal—toward, shall I say, the angelic. If you are allergic to angels, turn then toward the spiritual—broadly defined.

Let me name three examples of the many opportunities for readjusting our goals and horizons.

First, we have long given lip-service to the principle and command to love our fellow men, but practically we have not always liked the idea. Fellow man is often repugnant.

We keep away from most of him most of the time—we send small gifts. But the world has shrunk. In spite of political and other barriers, we are now all neighbors. The interest in, and love and respect for, off-color fellows of the human race is changed in character from that of a century ago. Conclusion: A *universal philanthropism* (brotherly compassion) is one of the new human horizons.

And here is another, which comes to us from the new cosmography. The plaguy astronomers have probed so deep and so far that we can no longer accept, without great uneasiness, the comfortable ideas about time and space of a few decades ago. We have been deposed by the scientists from physical importance in the universe, and made ephemeral and peripheral. No longer can there be much esteem on the cosmic scale for a vain and strutting man-animal. It is a hard pill to swallow, this cosmic humility, but we no longer doubt the facts. Our God (or gods, as the case may be, or Deity, or Nature, or First Cause) has much more on His (their, its) "hands" than a paternal concern for peripheral, transient, terrestrial primates—much more than the kindly care of the biota of one planet.

The Universe, it seems to me (whom am, by the way, a religious man—on my definition of religion), is much more glorious than the prophets of old reported, and we are actors in a greater show than the old billing led us to expect. Knowing what I now know, I would blush to be caught red-handed with the world concepts of two thousand years ago. And therefore, *a proper cosmic orientation* can be this second horizon, new to most of us.

Third, the human mind was considered fairly private until recently, largely because we did not know enough about it to justify its exhibition in the marketplace. But now the senses have been dissected; the electric currents of the nerves have been measured; brain waves have become diagnostic; and much of our inner life, that we thought was beyond the reach of measuring instruments, is out in plain sight on the drawing boards. Here we find another horizon that needs adjusting—both for those who talk and think of matters spiritual and for those who indulge themselves (and serve the rest of us) in the realms of the cultural arts. We must be more *mindful of the mind.*

Thus in these three sample realms—worldwide social relations, the physical universe, and the human mind—new opportunities arise for the adjustment of our horizons.

I have one general comment on the problem of making the adjustment. The ideals that spiritual leaders advocate are, in my opinion, of high importance—more important, in the long run, than the political ideals of our puzzled diplomats. In our biological program of establishing the Psychozoic Kingdom, the non-material grows in significance. Men and women of the churches are among the keepers of the non-material. Therefore, *openmindedness with respect to the growth and bearing of knowledge of the material world* is a high-priority requirement for your set of adjusted ideals. Openmindedness to the progress of the human intellect is the first ideal. Re-oriented piety is second, and follows naturally.

15

A Design for Fighting

In concluding this exploration of man's physical and spiritual place in the universe, I should like to offer comments on the behavior and aspirations of men at war. The comments may be not too tedious, for wars are never dull. I plan to deal mostly with fights that are outside the history books, and to suggest some worthy new enemies. But first we need to examine honestly our attitude toward war.

I shall begin by recounting a sad folk tale. Once upon a time (but recently) there was a great nation in a mess. When it struggled to disentangle itself from the condition that had been brought on by this and by that, the situation seemed to grow messier, and no less than 22 millions of its adults voted to change horses in the middle of the bog.

That nation's ills were everywhere obvious. A great many poor people were hungry, while other citizens destroyed their surpluses; more than ten million were unemployed; the desires of the laborers for greater pay and prestige were doing badly; the women without higher education were submerged by custom and lack of opportunity; the people had no thrifty desires to accumulate savings, and indeed, they had nothing much to save; the young men and women had little systematic training in health or in patriotism; they had little opportunity to travel. (You have guessed the nation's name?)

In this economically and spiritually confused country (we continue to list its ills), diseases like measles, pneumonia, and syphilis were badly controlled, if at all; mosquitoes and flies seemed destined to be eternal pests and carriers of disease; practically no one in all that nation could use radar, or anti-radar, or anti-anti-radar; social reforms were progressing with difficulty, and educational policy was static.

The airplanes were relatively slow and weak; the researches in the physical sciences throughout the country were listless; the art of shipbuilding and ship-sailing had practically disappeared. Worst of all, there was little zest for life and liberty, no driving principle or policy to make the citizens from all corners of the country proud to be citizens of that nation and brothers under a sun that might illuminate a hopeful future.

It was a somber epoch (that decade of the 1930s) in the history of a great nation, and the prospects for recovery and progress, and for the elimination of the enumerated evils, were dim indeed.

This chapter is based on a lecture delivered in 1943. A surprising number of the recommendations made in the original lecture have since been adopted.

A SUGGESTED THERAPY FOR HARD TIMES

If I had, at that time, ventured to suggest that the afflicted nation could remedy all these ills, every one of them, by entering into the greatest and bloodiest human war ever conceived—take part in a war that would destroy more property and brutally butcher more innocent people than the worst human butchers had ever enjoyed in their goriest dreams— if I had recommended that mad procedure, guaranteeing the almost complete cure of the enumerated ills within ten years, and guaranteeing the practical attainment of all the high goals I have implied, it is quite likely that both my advice and I would have been (to understate it) deplored. It is possible that some solicitous souls might have written letters to the Harvard authorities about their mad fanatics, recommending my transfer to an institution more suitable than a university.

Naturally, I did not make such a recommendation. Nevertheless, this nation did get into just such a war, and all of those evils and woes were promptly eliminated.

Probably never in the history of the United States have its people, as a whole, eaten so well as during the years 1940– 45. There was practically no unemployment. The thrill and even the joy of living were much increased. The nation became healthier. (The toll of those killed and maimed by the war was only of the same order of magnitude as the annual automobile casualties before the war.) The people rather willingly adopted healthy restraints, constructive collaboration, unified determination, a national spirit of worthy sacrifice. Sensational advances in the treatment of several diseases, new knowledge of food, new accomplishment in a million new home gardens, new and widespread instruction in world geography—all this also came as rewards of the war. Without that conflict, most of these benefits might still be totally missing, and the others only partly achieved. The women in the offices, factories, and armed services discovered abilities and self-assurance previously unrealized. Elementary applied sciences were taught to about a million young men in the armed forces who would otherwise have been deprived of the practical training that is important in a civilization highly dependent on applied science. The political and social prestige of labor increased remarkably in the years of war, and millions of citizens put billions of dollars into savings—establishing a nest-egg policy previously unknown, unpracticed, or impossible.

In the face of these manifold blessings for the majority of individuals in America, and the apparent social gains for the nation as a whole, who can sincerely regret the world war, and who would take steps to prevent a repetition? (I am speaking of ordinary world war—not of the atomic variety.) Should we not praise those who precipitated World War II? Do we know of any equivalent substitute for such a Beneficent War?

WHY NOT WAR AS A NATIONAL BUSINESS?

The problem must be examined further, or strange conclusions will be reached and astonishing national policies advocated.

Let us try to list the profits and losses. First, the profits. War was long ago recognized as a good tribal business by certain savage and primitive people. They fought for food,

women, loot, and the joy of personal combat. These are not
our American motives. We have food; we have, if anything,
too many women; our individual property holdings average
to be the richest in the world; the joy of *personal* combat has
been pretty well bred out of us, and even if it has not, modern
war provides little opportunity for personal blood-letting,
since even conventional wars are now about nine-tenths
fought on the draftsmen's boards, in the machine shop, and
by high-flying bombers. Less than a tenth of our mobilized
warriors in battlefields, factories, and farms ever smell the
human enemy or grapple with him. The poetry and romance
of combat, the snorting rush of the foaming charger, and
the wild, savage clash of sabers have been machined out of
modern wars. Most of the excitement, for most of us, is
vicarious. At the height of a hard-pressing crisis, we may
loyally work at the lathes some 54 hours a week—with time
and a half for overtime, of course.

The major gains from war are therefore not so elemental
as those that made war a national business for earlier tribes.
It is now not for food, loot, and glory that we fight, but (if
we judge by our successes) for the great social gains mentioned above—for widely-distributed prosperity, large wealth
for a new set of capitalists, and the provision of work for
everybody, with good pay for good work. Socially uplifting
was World World II, as well as materially profitable, for
more than 100 million Americans.

Up to this point, it sounds as if it would be folly not to
adopt world war as our permanent policy. The advantages
and dividends seem compelling. How, then, can we explain
the amazing situation that practically everyone fervently
hopes, apparently, that there will never again be another
world war, even of the non-atomic type?

(Undoubtedly there exist a few who secretly hope that wars will continue—a few scattered among the military officers, politicians, profiteering businessmen, and certain magnified personalities of the press and radio. But most of us classify such individuals as moral perverts, and not a creditable part of the American citizenry.)

What reasons can we find for the majority's abhorrence of war? It seems fairly clear that our antipathy is not based on worry about postwar economic effects, for successful wars are frequently followed by good times. We can, however, enumerate some social disadvantages:

1. War makes nearly all the members of the military establishment important, and sometimes overweeningly arrogant. The same is true of hundreds of Washington bureaucrats. This is probably a disadvantage to the American political and social system. After the war's end, it is pretty hard to demobilize the pride and belligerent spirit and habits of the glory-inflated, war-enriched members of our society.

2. Wars build politically minded veterans' organizations— again a net disadvantage.

3. Wars interfere with the normal care of children, and probably impair their morale.

4. The usual type of college education is interrupted for a few years for many boys. Presumably that should be listed as a disadvantage.

5. Although war improves the business of newspapers, radio, many manufacturers, the transportation and communications industries, and most small businessmen, it ruins some useful enterprises, at least temporarily. And the white-collar classes, as usual, suffer economically, because their intake lags behind their increased outgo.

6. Some would list "the economic waste of war" as a

frightful price to pay for full employment and full stomachs and purses.

7. Taxes become atrocious. In wartime, however, most of us pay the heavy taxes almost cheerfully, as a matter of healthful national discipline and as a willing contribution to the prevailing prosperity.

It is obvious that I am reaching around desperately for sufficient practical disadvantages to discredit war. To discover the really important reasons for the American people's present strong aversion to the war business, we must look further.

MORALITY ENTERS THE DESIGN

As I see it, there are two major reasons for not adopting war as the best national or international business. One is very obvious and the other leads toward hope for the human race.

1. Up to now, we in America have been on the winning side of all our foreign wars, and from the first we have known that we would win. Furthermore, these wars have not been on our home grounds. Those obvious factors explain much about our attitude—past and present. In Europe, practically none of the war's advantages cited above was available to the French, Dutch, Norwegians, Czechs, and other states that suffered occupation or conquest in World War II. Only a few advantages (such as full employment and perhaps unity of spirit) were enjoyed by the Axis countries before their defeat. Even Great Britain, though not conquered, reaped only a few of the gains that we reaped. We alone were able to keep our winning war at a distance. It was relatively a very profitable time for us, and not all the profits were temporary. For future wars the outlook is totally different. We have reasons to suspect that winning is no longer a certainty

—for us or for anyone else. And we know that with missiles now capable of flying over the oceans we could not keep a war away from our homeland.

2. As a hope-nourishing comment, I offer the proposition that a basic reason why 150 million Americans, and untold hundreds of millions of others, want an end of war is that they have become convinced that war *is immoral*. The moral objection outweighs all the presumed material and social benefits of war—the prosperity, the glory, the excitement— even for a winning nation. This is a fact of highest encouragement to all who are solicitous for the further evolution of the human race. It is inspiriting that we Americans, who temporarily gained so many worthwhile social and personal advantages, are nevertheless conscious of the cosmic error of it all.

We owe to two widely different causes our present consciousness of the long-range tragic penalties of war. One is the remarkably dramatic news coverage of wars by press and radio, which has not concealed from the happy Americans the bitter blood and tears. The other is the cumulative religious and secular education of the centuries, which has gradually built an intellectual heritage and a universal ethics which link peace with social justice, with international good will, and with human progress. Through moral education, peace has become an inherent human desire; it is almost an instinctive good for educated men, and war an instinctive evil.

No doubt there are other important factors that tend to overshadow for most people the social and material gains of war—even successful war at a distance. But personally I am content to accept the argument that the most cogent motive for abolishing war is the moral gain. The arguments against war based on economics and demography are too often specious and circular; usually they involve merely postponements and short-term compromises. The moral antipathy to war, on the other hand, is clearly a built-in product of the mental and spiritual development of mankind. I am gratified that we can rate it highly.

In the context of the thesis I am attempting to develop, I should not close this review of the profits and losses of human warfare without at least briefly asking the rather embarrassing question: Why did we fight the Second World War? Perhaps it suffices to say that in some comprehensive but vague way—made vague by detailed rationalizations—we fought for a civilization. Let us leave it at that, remembering again that there are better ways of fighting for civilization than international war with human and material devastation as the goal. And this leads me to my main thesis: We should produce a Design for Fighting future wars of a very different kind.

AN INGLORIOUS DEFEAT

In 1918–19 more than four times as many Americans were killed by influenza as by our enemies of the First World War. Over the world, 20 million humans perished of the ruthless disease. The economic loss in that worldwide battle with the influenza organism was also tremendous. Moreover, sad and shameful to say, we lost the war. We, the highest and most resourceful animals on the face of the earth, came off battered and disgraced, with the enemy hardly scratched. Only when the virus became satiated with its successes did it recede into the invisible realms where it normally dwells. Not permanently—from time to time since then it has emerged in further forays with murderous and economically destructive results. Our Maginot lines of defense against it remain permeable and insufficient.

Clearly we have right here a dangerous enemy that merits an all-out war. Why are we not all taking up arms against this treacherous foe—an enemy who does not hesitate to make sneak attacks and has no respect for armistice? Several hundred million of us were engaged in those influenza battles of 1918–19.

I now wonder why in heaven's name we casualties who survived and returned from those sniffling battlefields did not form an American Flu Legion, don our old face masks and march in parades, brandish our voting strength, and influence Congressmen. With our political power, under the leadership of *General* Doctor, of *Captain* Laboratory Technician, of *Lieutenant* Nurse—all who fought valiantly with us millions of suffering *privates* in the great influenza war— with that voting power we might have got the Government to fortify research laboratories munificently, drill the citizens in epidemic prevention and control, enforce the care of body and mind, and turn the powerful mass psychology into a fervent, patriotic assault on this enemy of mankind, which has always been more deadly than the soldiers of European fanatics and tyrants. So prepared, we would be ready for the next attack. We could sell Health Bonds, pay taxes luxuriously, work like the devil, and perhaps we would, this time, win the war, conquer our great enemy, and keep him subjugated for as long as man remains civilized and sanitary.

But, alas, we did not organize. Medical investigators and public health officers continue to do their best, without sufficient government or public support, while the undertakers year after year continue to tuck us away prematurely.

SELECTING ENEMIES FOR COMING WARS

The anti-flu battle, however, is only a skirmish compared to the wars I have in mind. The Design for Fighting I want to sketch for you is not so simple and obvious as would be a defensive war against an epidemic disease. To fight defensively means admission of intellectual defeat. I want to go deeper. We should remember that it is only the bodies of men and women that the gravediggers inter and the cremators oxidize. Our civilized heritage, our contributions to knowledge and to the art and beauty of human living—our spirits, if you will—escape the mortuary. Our works live after us. Why not, therefore, seek out some of the enemies that assail those human qualities that we group loosely under the term civilization?

Let us look up the opponents to the evolution of the human characteristics that seem to differentiate men from other animals and plants. We may discover that an enthusiastic warfare against such opponents, even if only partly successful, is a fair substitute for warfare against fellow men. At least such conflicts would emphasize the absurdity of political wars, in which life and property are wildly squandered while these greater enemies—the enemies of the soul, mind, sometimes body—are almost completely ignored.

Instinctive and acquired human morality, as we have already noted, seems to oppose the promotion of man-kill-man war, but this same inherent morality, I am certain, is vigorously pro-war—war to the death—against those enemies that obstruct or challenge the social and intellectual growth of man and of human society.

In designing a fight, it is comforting to feel that "right is on our side." Unfortunately, this familiar claim has a hollow ring. It is the conscience-salve of provocateurs everywhere and every time. Kings, kaisers, cardinals, cutthroats, and even we minor squabblers have always taken comfort in the claimed benign assistance of God, the eternal righteousness of our cause, and a holy justification of our murderous actions. Very well, we shall leave Omnipotence out of our wars. Instead, we shall enlist on our side Nature, or Creative Evolution, or the Primal and Persisting Urge of the human species to evolve during the billions of years that the stars appear to have allotted us.

We could, of course, betray this evolutionary cause, deliberately refuse to grow, and go turtling through the ages, dull and static; we could even regress, like a petered-out biological species, by way of recurrent world wars and social degradations. But it is better cosmic sportsmanship and more exciting to go to the top, to the limit of our abilities and aspirations, for there may be something at that rainbow's end that will make even the galaxies look trivial.

Whatever the postulates in which we clothe ourselves, whether our tailors are religious prophets, pagan philosophers, modern scientific cosmogonists, or the still striving spirit of jungle-born curiosity, the majority of Americans are already amply dressed for the uphill climb. We can put on varied armor to suit the fight.

This presumed readiness of the citizen-soldiers is a challenge to anyone who ventures to propose campaigns and strategies. We should choose opponents worthy of the steel and spirit of determined and intelligent men. No boastful pacification of a restless island will suffice, no capture of a distant market for the enriching of a few traders, no gloating superiority in nuclear missiles. Those are goals of an old-fashioned type, unworthy, unsuited to human dignity in this time of a New Renaissance. No, it has got to be good, this set of plans; our real enemies and strategies must be chosen carefully.

These new conflicts, moreover, must not be local wars, for a few scientific laboratories, or for one country or one county. The fight must be international. We can enlist in all countries an army of potential allies, willing, well-armed, and similarly star-bent. For the opening phase of our campaign I shall mention four obstructive enemies, the conquest of which would make the rest of the fight much easier. They are Illiteracy, Premature Senility, Cultural Uniformity, and the greatest of all—The Tyranny of the Unknown.

ILLITERACY

Education is always well spoken of. Although it is frequently misguided into anti-social channels, it is by and large both good and necessary—indeed, indispensable if democracy is to prevail and the dignity of the individual is to be respected and enhanced. Literacy is basic for democracy. Notwithstanding the rapid rise of auditory education by way of the radio, and of pictorial education by moving pictures and television, there is no reasonable escape from the general necessity of knowing how to read and write. Even a tabloid newspaper requires a modicum of literacy, and the comic strips carry printed matter.

The point I am driving at is that illiteracy can and should be wiped out. The basic equipment (reading and writing) for general and special education should be universally provided. It is not a job for the regular school teachers alone. It is a national job, for the public and the local governments.

Ten years from now the existence of illiteracy between the ages of ten and 60 in any civilized country (including the United States) should be reckoned as a disgrace. The shame should be on the community, on the country, and not on the unfortunate individuals. In many communities, perhaps most, volunteer teachers, performing a sympathetic rather than a patronizing task, could take care of this business without difficulty.

In Mexico, an enlightened president, General Manuel Avila Camacho, once requested educated adults to undertake, as a part of their national service, the elementary education of at least one unschooled neighbor. Must other countries lag behind in social growth? Must they await a presidential order? A command from the conscience of the community should suffice. The people can do this work with pleasure and with justifiable pride. And once the first battle, for universal literacy, has been won, the aim can be raised and a further step taken toward an enlightened citizenry. The second goal might be: "80 per cent of those older than 15 years must have completed a grammar school education." For this achievement there should be a ceremonious bestowal, to each successful community, of an "E" for Excellent, or Education, or Evolving.

The important problem of illiteracy should not be left wholly to educators. We are all involved. I wonder if sufficient thought has been given to rewards for community successes, to the enlisting of the interest of service groups, and to the expert selling of the enterprise to the general public.

There may be, of course, an irreducible minimum of illiteracy, perhaps 1 per cent, because of insurmountable physical disabilities and the presence in the community of illiterate transients. But the occurrence of foreign-language

elements in a community should be no excuse for not under-
taking or solving this problem; rather it should be a challenge, and an opportunity for mutual education.

PREMATURE SENILITY

As a second martial enterprise, let us declare war on Premature Senility. The more we study the life spans and the
death causes of Americans and Europeans, the more we
realize that a few maladies and a few bad habits cut off too
many useful people prematurely. Most of us say that we
would dread the prolongation of useless old age, but who
can object to the adding of ten years to the active lives of
men and women to whom the years have brought augmented
wisdom, and in whom experience has produced nobility of
character?

I look forward to the time, perhaps in a century or so,
when an adult caught with a communicable disease will be
heavily fined, and one indulging in afflictions like cancer,
tuberculosis, arthritis, and neuroses will be branded as a social pariah, and put in jail. I would like to hope that the
names of some of those diseases will become so little known
that one would find them only at the bottom of the dictionary
page—"cancer: obsolescent name for a rare disease, rampant
in the dark ages; as late as 1960 it was killing 150,000 Americans annually." But my hope is perhaps too wild. Certainly
there will need to be some hard fighting and heavy expense
and further education before that Utopia dawns.

The Western world is not overpopulated; there is ahead
useful work of noble note—joys to be shared, fine thoughts
to be meditated, sunsets for everybody. The proper balance
for a diminishing but healthily-controlled birthrate could be

the prolongation of adult life. Already the medical and health sciences have done astonishing work on the diseases of infancy. The average age of the population has risen spectacularly in America and elsewhere. But mature men and women will live and work happily half a generation longer when, as the result of a sincere and widespread war, we conquer or control arthritis, cancer, nephritis, diseases and disorders of the circulatory system, of the respiratory system, and of the brain. These six are the chief disablers.

In the United States six million people suffer from the various forms of arthritis, and hundreds of thousands are prematurely disabled thereby. Cancer kills an average of 400 Americans each day—more than the daily loss of American lives (300) in the critical eleven days of the bloody battle of Normandy in 1944. An enemy that destroys 400 lives a day, with the accompaniment of great suffering, sorrow, and expense, justifies a much larger war budget than we now provide for this fight. The same is true for our deadly enemy, the disease of the circulatory system, from which half a million Americans die each year. And for fighting our greatest enemy among the major maladies, the mental illnesses that disorder and spoil the human mind, we are spending almost nothing at all at the research level.

Yet progress is being made against these killers, despite our indifferent support, and there is reason to expect dramatic further advances. But without public help, complete victory will be impossible. We of the public can make notable contributions in three ways. We can inspire brilliant young scientists to enlist, preferably as volunteers, in this great war for human life and happiness. We can provide directly by gift, or indirectly through influencing governmental support, the necessary funds for the hospitals, research laboratories, and field studies. We can cooperate in controlling some of these scourges by taking care of personal health and by seeing to it that our communities are provided with appropriate health programs.

Without further documentation, let us acknowledge the need for a concerted national attack on the recognizable causes of Premature Senility—the ailment that sooner or later will be of personal interest to practically all of us. Would you like to have one-tenth of 1 per cent of your future federal income tax devoted to the elimination, or at least the great diminution, of the ills that prematurely weaken and destroy? Would you participate in an annual "one-meal fast" to pay for research on the major maladies? If we all took part, and contributed the equivalent of about 15 million dollars, we could win years of additional life and happiness, because several deadly diseases would die.

CULTURAL UNIFORMITY

I would like to isolate another conflict in which everybody can take part. We can call it the Fight Against Cultural Uniformity. It would take long to elaborate fully the need for this movement, and still longer to specify sample procedures in detail. Here a brief summary must suffice; I have already discussed the subject to some extent in Chapter 13.

Life, I have found from experience, has a tendency to lapse into stupefying dullness. It would be vastly duller but for variety among the people one meets, diversity in their habits, manners, and intellectual reactions. To maintain and increase the diversity, to the end of enhancing the degree of satisfaction with life and the opportunity for intellectual and artistic growth, requires immediate fighting against real foes.

We must oppose those tendencies that are working toward standardization and cultural homogeneity. We must strive against chain-thinking and chain-acting. As a contribution to this objective, our local communities must grow in cultural self-sufficiency, not only for the delight of the people in being doers rather than in being done-for, but also because of the importance of endemic culture to general welfare.

The responsibility for the fight against cultural uniformity devolves finally on the community itself. In this connection it is well to study the successes of the Tennessee Valley Authority, the progress of the community theater movement, the future of television broadcasting.

In the contest against deadening centralized manipulation of the minds and mores of the people, we have a happy fight that all can join. Paradoxically enough, nationally active artists and scientists can help to incite diversity and direct the development of local cultural projects; the radio and press syndicates can assist in spreading the gospel of community self-sufficiency.

THE TYRANNY OF THE UNKNOWN

We come now to the fourth scheme for combat. I may be obsessed, or suffering from anthropocentric illusions, but I cannot escape the feeling that the human mind and human curiosity are significant in this world—even perhaps in the cosmos of geological time and intergalactic space. With this impression (or illusion) that the human mind is the best of us, and the best of biological evolution, I cannot escape (and neither can you!) the feeling of a responsibility to glorify the human mind, take it seriously, even dream about its ultimate flowering into something far beyond the primitive muscle-guider and sensation-recorder with which we started.

Perhaps it is naive to insist that the acquiring of knowledge and sensations is a human necessity, and it is elementary to observe that in the short time the race has had for reasoning about things, it has been impossible to learn much. Time has been just too short. But pointing out such elementals gives us background, and perhaps modesty. We are still embedded in abysmal ignorance of the world in which we live. Relative to the total surmisable extent of knowledge, we have advanced very little beyond the level of wisdom acquired by many animals. We are, to be sure, not often afraid now of strange squeaks in the dark, nor completely superstitious about the dead. On many occasions we are valiantly rational. Moreover, we know "how much the unknown transcends the what we know." The unrevealed seriously oppresses us as men of mind. We are tyrannized by the unanswered more than by governmental restraints or social taboos. This tyranny dims the brightest of the explored realms of nature. Let's exorcise these tyrannical spirits of the surrounding darkness. Let's declare a methodical and elaborate war on the Tyranny of the Unknown.

Already, in our quiet way, most scientists are mildly opposing this tyranny. We do it in our spare time, sometimes apologetically, and sometimes with the rather brave and hopeful sanction of our institutional chiefs. But except when we have war-urgency assignments, we do not let the Tyranny fight get in the way of comfortable living, routine duties, and our ordinary neighborliness.

I trust that you do not get the impression that I am advocating merely an intensification of our present enterprise

of scientific research. That is not at all what I have in mind.
I mean, I repeat, "a *methodical* and *elaborate* warfare on the
Tyranny of the Unknown."

It is time we stopped treating the acquisition of new
knowledge as the luxury of a special class, or as the precursor
to profit-makng new gadgets or nostrums. It is time we quit
leaving the explorations beyond the horizons to the long-
haired professors and the workers in a few government bureaus. The contest with the Tyranny of the Unknown is a
job for the people of the United States of America, if they
are going to keep up in the competition with other countries
and if they are planning to participate in either the practical
or the idealized progress of mankind. It should be the concern of the businessman, the labor union, the fruit grower,
and the farmer. This war can be an affair for a Popular Front,
if the proper leaders properly blueprint the campaign. Practically every community in America that can produce an
armed ensign or a sergeant could also produce a boy or girl
who could be trained to effective, even if modest, service
in these new research armies. Once the attack is briefed and
the skills are sharpened, finding new facts and checking old
interpretations will be no more difficult than making an
automobile from blueprints, or managing intership communications, or unravelling the mysteries of an income tax
form. Yes, certainly the increase and spreading out of scientific and other research is a national concern, and, in making
this a national issue, respect for fundamentals need not be
sacrificed to the utilitarian.

Fortunately, not many conscientious scholars feel that the
increase of knowledge is for the elite alone. But we are not
yet adequately prepared to open the systematic and enduring campaign against this Enemy Number One. There must

be several preliminary preparations, which will take labor, thought, and time:

1. The crusade must be sold to the average citizen, through skillful propaganda (or education, if you prefer that term). We must discover appeals to the imagination and the emotions. We need systematic research on the methods of creating understanding and sympathy for research. We must discover ways to make the fight against the Tyranny of the Unknown a national issue, like good government and individual freedom.

2. Local and national governments must be convinced of the merit of this cause, and of the importance of increasing official support for the mobilization of appropriate forces and resources.

3. The schools and colleges must recognize the importance of producing critical scholars and creative thinkers. They must see that one man fired with curiosity is worth much more than two solid and stolid citizens.

4. The Design for Fighting must be prepared. It must be outlined and published to the collaborating workers. It may require the leadership of a new institution—an Academy of Intellectual Exploration.

Among the citizens of America are many thousands who are the special agents of the people and of the civilization they compose. These servants of society are the teachers who have been trained, mostly at the expense of the public, to know what is known and what is not.

It is to these several thousand servant-thinkers that I now put the question I set out to ask: Would it be advisable and possible to list *in extenso* for each of scores of special fields of knowledge the unsolved problems immediately before us?

The question requires elaboration. The proposed listing would be for technical specialists chiefly, and less directly, or only incidentally, for the non-specialist. Probably in all fields there are many able workers who for one reason or another do not have a grasp of neighboring areas, or even a full picture of their own subject. These workers may be young and as yet inexperienced, or they may be isolated scholars, away from discussion groups and large laboratories and libraries. Important fields often are thoroughly comprehended by only a few intense workers who have favorable temperaments and opportunities.

Everybody gains if the obstacles to enriched research are removed. Would not such detailed clarification through problem-listing be worth doing for the benefit of both the beginner and the professional? What are the immediate unknowns, practical and theoretical, that might be subdued if they were fully recognized and if an abundance of thinkers and resources were available to grapple with them? For example, there are exciting fields in mammalian anatomy, in atomic structure, in the amelioration of insanity, in regional planning, in pre-Cambrian stratigraphy, in the history of printing devices, in the phylogeny of the anthropoids, in aeronautics, in group tensions, in meteorology, in the use of leisure. In all these areas the Unknown still challenges us.

We will be shortsighted indeed if we do not adopt a national policy of investigating so that, with the tools of science and cultural education, we can undertake holy wars here at home against our non-human enemies, which have long held us down physically and frustrated our social evolution.

RESOURCES FOR WAR-MAKING

Our true enemies are not men or nations but poverty, disease, suspicion, and ignorance. These are the worldwide antagonists that, in the twentieth century, can be considered foreign and most dangerous to the human condition. We now have efficient weapons for overcoming them. And we can also enlist in this war, as powerful assets, the same human qualities that have operated so destructively in the past: namely, combativeness, the thrill of contest, and the instinct to survive.

The institution of warfare is, of course, older than man himself. The defeatists among us grimly say that war is a natural, immutable instinct. I do not myself subscribe heartily to the argument that, because men have always fought wars, there is no hope that they will abandon this barbaric habit. But even if hate and warfare are deep, unyielding instincts, can we not channel these powerful forces in constructive directions? Can we not hook up those inborn energies to a Design for Fighting a greater war—a war against the foes of all mankind?

We are now nearly perfectly equipped for such a war with five winning weapons; they are man's instinctive combativeness, the instinct for survival, our rich experience in the organization of manpower and equipment on a massive scale, our advanced skills in many fields, and our ability to mobilize the abundance of our planet's natural resources. Against this richness of mental and material armaments, what chance would the enemies of our species have in a war into which we threw the same intelligence and savage determination that we invested in the Second World War?

Hundreds of billions of dollars and hundreds of billions

of man-hours went into the destroying of man and his works between 1939 and 1945. With just 1 per cent of the resources, fervor, and self-sacrifice that we devoted to the murderous enterprises of those desperate years, we could construct a civilization of which *Homo sapiens* could indeed be proud. There would be no losers in such a war for the health, sanity, and comfort of the inhabitants of our planet; and the Earth, though only a minor object in one small corner of the immense universe of planets, stars, and galaxies, would flourish as the home of ambitious mankind.

Index